THE ULTIMATE
SEATTLE SEAHAWKS
TRIVIA BOOK

A Collection of Amazing Trivia Quizzes
and Fun Facts for Die-Hard Seahawks Fans!

Ray Walker

Exclusive Free Book
Crazy Sports Stories

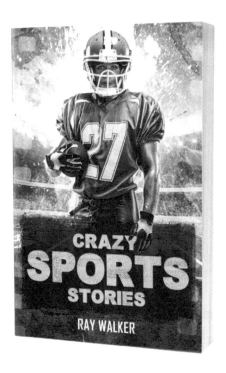

As a thank you for getting a copy of this book I would like to offer you a free copy of my book Crazy Sports Stories which comes packed with interesting stories from your favorite sports such as Football, Hockey, Baseball, Basketball and more.

Grab your free copy over at
RayWalkerMedia.com/Bonus

CONTENTS

INTRODUCTION

The Seahawks were established in 1976 in Seattle, Washington. The Hawks have consistently proven themselves to be a team that fights hard and is a force to be reckoned with in the NFL, especially in the 2010s.

They currently hold one Super Bowl championships, which they won in 2013. They have won three NFC Conference championships, eight NFC West Division championships, and two AFC West Division championships. They are very often a threat in the NFC West, having last won it in 2016. They have made 18 NFL playoff appearances total, with their most recent Super Bowl appearance coming in 2014.

The Seahawks have retired the uniform numbers of the 12th Man (Seahawks fans), Kenny Easley, Walter Jones, Steve Largent, and Cortez Kennedy.

The thing about football is that it is a lot like life. There are good times and bad times, good days and bad days, but you have to do your absolute best to never give up. The Seattle Seahawks have proven that they refuse to give up and that they will do anything they need to do to bring a championship to the state of Washington. Winning is more than possible when you have a storied past as the Seahawks

1

do. They have so much captivating history and so many undeniable player legacies to be profoundly proud of.

The Seahawks' current home is CenturyLink Field, which opened in 2002. They play in one of the most difficult divisions in the NFL, the NFC West, alongside the San Francisco 49ers, Los Angeles Rams, and Arizona Cardinals.

With such a rich past that goes back generations, you're probably already very knowledgeable as the die-hard 12th Man that you are. Let's test that knowledge to see if you truly are the world's biggest Seahawks fan.

CHAPTER 1:

ORIGINS & HISTORY

QUIZ TIME!

1. Which of the following team names did the Seahawks franchise once go by?

    a. Mariners

    b. Sonics

    c. Water Bugs

    d. None of the above; they have always been the Seahawks

2. In what year was the Seattle Seahawks franchise established?

    a. 1949

    b. 1955

    c. 1976

    d. 1980

3. The Seahawks' current home stadium is CenturyLink Field.

    a. True

    b. False

4. In which division do the Seattle Seahawks play?

    a. NFC West
    b. AFC West
    c. NFC North
    d. AFC North

5. The Seattle Seahawks were a member of the AFC West Division from 1977 to 2001.

    a. True
    b. False

6. How many NFC championships has the Seahawks franchise won (as of the end of the 2019 season)?

    a. 2
    b. 3
    c. 6
    d. 9

7. What is the name of the Seahawks' mascot?

    a. Blue
    b. Squatch
    c. Blitz
    d. Seahawk Sam

8. Who is the winningest head coach in Seattle Seahawk history (as of 2020 season)?

    a. Mike Holmgren
    b. Pete Carroll
    c. Dennis Erickson
    d. Chuck Knox

9. Seattle Seahawks fans are often referred to as the
   _____.

   a. 12th Man
   b. SeaHollers
   c. Hawks Homies
   d. Hawkers

10. Who was the first head coach of the Seattle Seahawks'
    franchise?

    a. Mike Holmgren
    b. Chuck Knox
    c. Pete Carroll
    d. Jack Patera

11. Seahawks fans have set the Guinness World Record for the
    loudest crowd noise at a sporting event not only once, but
    twice.

    a. True
    b. False

12. What is the name of the Seahawks' practice facility?

    a. AdventHealth Training Center
    b. Virginia Mason Athletic Center
    c. Quest Diagnostics Training Center
    d. Under Armour Performance Center

13. How many appearances has the Seattle Seahawks
    franchise made in the NFL playoffs (as of the end of the
    2019 season)?

    a. 9
    b. 11

c. 15

d. 18

14. How many Super Bowl titles have the Seahawks won (as of the end of the 2019 season)?

    a. 0

    b. 1

    c. 2

    d. 3

15. The Seahawks never won an AFC West title during their time in that division.

    a. True

    b. False

16. Which was the first home stadium of the Seattle Seahawks franchise?

    a. Safeco Field

    b. CenturyLink Field

    c. Husky Stadium

    d. Kingdome

17. How many NFC West Division titles have the Seattle Seahawks won (as of the end of the 2019 season)?

    a. 3

    b. 6

    c. 8

    d. 9

18. Who is the current head coach of the Seattle Seahawks?

   a. Pete Carroll
   b. Chuck Knox
   c. Mike Holmgren
   d. Jack Patera

19. Russell Wilson is the current quarterback of the Seattle Seahawks (as of the 2020 season).

   a. True
   b. False

20. The Seahawks are the only NFL team based in the Pacific Northwest region of North America.

   a. True
   b. False

QUIZ ANSWERS

1. D – None of the above, they have always been the Seahawks

2. C – 1976

3. A – True

4. A – NFC West

5. A – True

6. B – 3

7. C – Blitz

8. B – Pete Carroll

9. A – 12th Man

10. D – Jack Patera

11. A – True

12. B – Virginia Mason Athletic Center

13. D – 18

14. B – 1

15. B – False (1988 and 1999)

16. D – Kingdome

17. C – 8

18. A – Pete Carroll

19. A – True

20. A – True

DID YOU KNOW?

1. The Seahawks franchise has had eight head coaches: Jack Patera, Mike McCormack, Chuck Knox, Tom Flores, Dennis Erickson, Mike Holmgren, Jim L. Mora, and Pete Carroll.

2. The Seahawks' current head coach is Pete Carroll. He has previously been the head coach of the New England Patriots, New York Jets, and USC Trojans. Carroll is one of only three head coaches who have won both a Super Bowl and a College Football National championship.

3. Pete Carroll is the Seattle Seahawks' all-time winningest head coach with a current record of 105-59-1.

4. Steve Largent was the first player to have his number retired by the Seattle Seahawks. His No. 80 was retired in 1992.

5. Neither Seattle nor the Seahawks have ever hosted the Super Bowl.

6. In 1984, No. 12 was retired by the Seahawks franchise to honor the fans, who are often referred to as the "12th Man."

7. The Seattle Seahawks have made three Super Bowl appearances. In the Super Bowls they have appeared in, they have faced the Pittsburgh Steelers, Denver Broncos, and New England Patriots.

8. The current owner of the Seattle Seahawks is the Paul

Allen Trust. Allen was best known for co-founding the Microsoft Corporation with his childhood friend, Bill Gates.

9. The Seahawks' mascot, Blitz, is a seahawk himself. He has been known to jump off the roof of CenturyLink Field and fly with the Blue Angels.

10. Kenny Easley is the latest Seahawk to have his number retired by the team. His number 45 was retired in 2017. Easley refused to let the Seahawks retire his number for years.

CHAPTER 2:

JERSEYS & NUMBERS

QUIZ TIME!

1. An all-navy uniform is currently the Seahawks' primary uniform option for home games.

    a. True
    b. False

2. The Seahawks' current team colors are _____, _____, and _____.

    a. Navy, forest green, and cold grey
    b. Blue, lime green, and grey
    c. College navy, action green, and wolf grey
    d. Baby blue, army green, and slim grey

3. On September 27, 2009, the Seahawks wore lime green jerseys for the first time, paired with dark navy-blue pants.

    a. True
    b. False

4. Which of the following numbers is NOT retired by the Seattle Seahawks (as of the 2019 season)?

    a. 12
    b. 71
    c. 80
    d. 95

5. What uniform number does QB Russell Wilson currently wear as a member of the Seahawks?

    a. 2
    b. 3
    c. 4
    d. 5

6. What uniform number did Richard Sherman wear during his time with the Seahawks?

    a. 1
    b. 5
    c. 15
    d. 25

7. Kenny Easley's No. 45 was retired by the Seahawks in 2017.

    a. True
    b. False

8. What uniform number did Golden Tate wear during his time with the Seahawks?

    a. 71
    b. 78

    c. 81

    d. 88

9. What uniform number did Marshawn Lynch wear during his time with the Seahawks?

    a. 23

    b. 24

    c. 25

    d. 27

10. The No. 12 was retired by the Seahawks for the fans, who are referred to as "the 12th Man."

    a. True

    b. False

11. Walter Jones' No. 71 was retired by the Seahawks in _____.

    a. 2010

    b. 2011

    c. 2012

    d. 2014

12. Who was the first Seahawks player to have his uniform number retired by the team?

    a. Cortez Kennedy

    b. Kenny Easley

    c. Steve Largent

    d. Walter Jones

13. Cortez Kennedy's No.96 was retired by the Seahawks in 2012.

a. True

b. False

14. What uniform number does Bobby Wagner currently wear for the Seahawks?

    a. 50

    b. 54

    c. 58

    d. 64

15. What uniform number did Jacob Green wear with the Seahawks?

    a. 66

    b. 69

    c. 76

    d. 79

16. What uniform number did Eugene Robinson wear when he was with the Seahawks?

    a. 31

    b. 41

    c. 51

    d. 61

17. What uniform number did Joe Nash wear while playing for the Seahawks?

    a. 72

    b. 62

    c. 52

    d. 42

18. What uniform number did Dave Krieg wear during his time with the Seahawks?

    a. 7

    b. 12

    c. 17

    d. 22

19. What uniform number did Matt Hasselbeck wear during his time with the Seahawks?

    a. 2

    b. 4

    c. 8

    d. 18

20. The Seahawks currently have retired five uniform numbers. (As of the 2020 season)

    a. True

    b. False

QUIZ ANSWERS

1. A - True

2. C – College navy, action green, and wolf grey

3. A – True

4. D – 95

5. B – 3

6. D – 25

7. A – True

8. C – 81

9. B – 24

10. A – True

11. A – 2010

12. C – Steve Largent (1992)

13. A – True

14. B – 54

15. D – 79

16. B – 41

17. A – 72

18. C – 17

19. C – 8

20. A – True

DID YOU KNOW?

1. The Seahawks have retired five numbers overall: The Fans (No. 12), Kenny Easley (No. 45), Walter Jones (No. 71), Steve Largent (No. 80), and Cortez Kennedy (No. 96).

2. During his time with the Seahawks, Jeff Bryant wore No. 77.

3. As a Seahawk, Dave Brown wore No. 22.

4. Rashaad Penny currently wears No. 20 for the Seattle Seahawks.

5. In 2016, the Seahawks unveiled the NFL Color Rush uniform, an all-action green uniform.

6. In 2012, when Nike took over NFL uniforms from Reebok, the Seahawks were left with nine different uniform combinations. This is when college navy, action green, and wolf grey were established as the team's colors. The Nike uniforms incorporate feathers, including 12 feathers on the neckline and pantlegs to represent the fans (12th Man).

7. On December 6, 2009, the Seahawks debuted their blue jersey with dark navy pants for the first time in a game against the San Francisco 49ers.

8. The Seahawks are currently the only team in NFL history to have worn their white jerseys at home.

9. Beginning in 2001, the Seahawks logos have been sewn on instead of being screen-printed.

10. During Super Bowl XL, the Seahawks wore their blue home jerseys even though they were the visitors because the Pittsburgh Steelers opted to wear their white jerseys.

CHAPTER 3:

FAMOUS QUOTES

QUIZ TIME!

1. Which current Seahawks player once said: "I'm not telling you it's going to be easy; I'm telling you it's going to be worth it"?

    a. Tre Flowers
    b. Carlos Hyde
    c. Russell Wilson
    d. D.K. Metcalf

2. Which former Seahawks player once said: "If you put in the work, put in the time, put in the effort, you're going to reap the benefits"?

    a. Walter Jones
    b. Richard Sherman
    c. Steve Largent
    d. Marshawn Lynch

3. Steve Largent once said: "Winners, I am convinced, imagine their dreams first. They want it with all their heart

and expect it to come true. There is, I believe, no other way to win."

a. True

b. False

4. Which Seahawks head coach once said: "It's about being the very best you can be. Nothing else matters as long as you're working and striving to be your best. Always compete. It's truly that simple. Find the way to do your best. Compete in everything you do"?

a. Pete Carroll

b. Jack Patera

c. Mike Holmgren

d. Jim L. Mora

5. Which former Seahawks player once said: "Today I will do what others won't, so tomorrow I can accomplish what others can't"?

a. Cortez Kennedy

b. Jerry Rice

c. Matt Hasselbeck

d. Golden Tate

6. Which former Seahawks player is quoted as saying: "I think leadership is more than being able to cross the T's and dot the I's. It's about character and integrity and work ethic"?

a. Richard Sherman

b. Cortez Kennedy

c. Eugene Robinson

d. Steve Largent

7. Which former Seahawks quarterback is quoted as saying: "When you get frustrated, you try too much. You try to make up stuff that's not there, and you play outside yourself"?

   a. Dave Krieg

   b. Jim Zorn

   c. Matt Hasselbeck

   d. Rick Mirer

8. Former Seahawk Dave Krieg once said, "Pressure is something you feel when you don't know what the hell you're doing."

   a. True

   b. False

9. Which Seahawks head coach once said: "Listen to what I tell you and do it. If you do, three things can happen: One, it will work, and you'll get credit. Two, it won't work, and I'll get the blame. Three, you'll do it wrong and you'll be gone"?

   a. Mike Holmgren

   b. Pete Carroll

   c. Chuck Knox

   d. Jim L. Mora

10. "I'm just here so I won't get _____." – Marshawn Lynch

a. Fired

b. Skittles

c. Traded

d. Fined

11. Which current Seahawks player is quoted as saying: "People have expectations of me… but at the end of the day, I don't have to live up to those expectations. All I have to do is go out there and be me"?

a. D.K. Metcalf

b. Tyler Lockett

c. Russell Wilson

d. Jason Myers

12. Which former Seahawks player is quoted as saying, "We don't really care what our critics say, we just enjoy proving them wrong and also proving ourselves right"?

a. Ricardo Lockette

b. Jermaine Kearse

c. Doug Baldwin

d. Percy Harvin

13. Which former Seahawks running back is quoted as saying: "I am a better running back every time I step on the field. I try to get better each game, each summer, each season"?

a. Curt Warner

b. Shaun Alexander

c. Marshawn Lynch

d. Ricky Watters

14. Which former Seahawks player is quoted as saying: "I have to keep inspiration close to me. I'm always on YouTube looking at the greats or anything that can give me the spark that I need"?

    a. Earl Thomas
    b. Jon Ryan
    c. Will Tukuafu
    d. Jermaine Kearse

15. Which Seahawks player was Richard Sherman referring to when he said: "We're a bunch of wild dogs until the big lion comes and then we're bad, we're some bad men with him around. He just brings that menacing force. We're a bunch of wild dogs and a pack of wild dogs is pretty dangerous. But a lion running with a pack of wild dogs, that's something"?

    a. Russell Wilson
    b. Marshawn Lynch
    c. Jermaine Kearse
    d. Kam Chancellor

16. Former Seahawk Curt Warner once said, "If you aren't going all the way, why go at all?"

    a. True
    b. False

17. Which former Seahawk is quoted as saying: "Sportsmanship is making sure you have respect for the guy you're playing across from"?

a. Michael Bennett

b. Warren Moon

c. Jim Zorn

d. Bobby Wagner

18. "_____ has got a tremendous competitive mindset and it stems from the confidence that he feels based on the preparation he puts." – Pete Carroll

a. Marshawn Lynch

b. D.K. Metcalf

c. Russell Wilson

d. Carlos Hyde

19. Which former Seahawks player once said: "Every day I feel lucky to have been drafted by the Seahawks. We have a crazy team with some chaotic dudes – a bunch of alphas"?

a. Golden Tate

b. Russell Wilson

c. Kam Chancellor

d. Richard Sherman

20. When giving advice to younger players, Marshawn Lynch once said: "Take care of y'all mentals, y'all bodies, y'all chicken, so when y'all ready to walk away, y'all walk away and you'll be able to do what y'all want to do."

a. True

b. False

QUIZ ANSWERS

1. C – Russell Wilson

2. B – Richard Sherman

3. B – False (Joe Montana)

4. C – Terry Francona

5. B – Jerry Rice

6. D – Steve Largent

7. C – Matt Hasselbeck

8. B – False (Peyton Manning)

9. A – Mike Holmgren

10. D – Fined

11. B – Tyler Lockett

12. C – Doug Baldwin

13. B – Shaun Alexander

14. A – Earl Thomas

15. D – Kam Chancellor

16. B – False, Joe Namath

17. B – Warren Moon

18. C – Russell Wilson

19. D – Richard Sherman

20. A – True

DID YOU KNOW?

1. "Growing up in Boston, I was always Matt, son of former New England Patriot Don. Then when my brother Tim was a senior in high school, I became Matt, brother of Tim." – Matt Hasselbeck

2. "I might not be a great athlete, but I think I'm a real good football player." – Steve Largent

3. "Marshawn Lynch is the heart of this team. If he's not going, the Seahawks aren't going." – Deion Sanders

4. "I just remember thinking, whichever team picked me I was going to make the other 31 regret it." – Russell Wilson

5. "Parents, teach your children to express themselves. Teach them to be in touch with their emotions, to speak honestly to people, and to maintain integrity and stick by their principles in all they do. This is perhaps the highest morality you can instill." – Jeff Bryant

6. "Now, I have to confess, I may be a tad bit biased on this next subject, but to the greatest football fans in the history of the NFL that occupied the old Kingdome back in the '70s and the '80s, and now CenturyLink Field, they call themselves the 12s, I say thank you. You guys made and still make pro football really fun in the Pacific Northwest." – Kenny Easley in his Pro Football Hall of Fame induction address

7. "Football has been a blessing. It has changed my life and those around me. It is a bond that keeps a family together and provided opportunities where there was just inspiration and determination. The thing I've learned along this incredible journey, I'm not only cheering for the rest of my life but pass it on to anyone that loves the game. Thank you, go Seahawks, and I love Seattle." – Walter Jones in his Pro Football Hall of Fame induction address

8. "This day, right now, this moment, it's always about those who came a long way, those who provided support, and those who have cheered, it's all about the 12th Man. It's all about those before, and who will come after. It's all about my beautiful daughter, Courtney. It is all about the players and friends I laughed with over the years. It is about all my teammates I cried with over the years, both in victory and defeat. It's not about winning or losing. It's so much bigger than that. It's about the relationship and about sharing it and working hard together. It's about not taking the shortcut. God bless America, and God bless the Seattle Seahawks. Thank you very much." – Cortez Kennedy in his Pro Football Hall of Fame induction address

9. "You know, my most significant accomplishments have always come in the context of a team. And I also want to thank my teammates in victory and defeat, especially Jim Zorn and Dave Krieg, who are both here this afternoon.

   But I also want to share with you, briefly this afternoon, the message of my life. My story, like so many others, is a story of mentors -- of people who challenged me when I questioned myself, of people who believed in me against all the evidence: my mother who never missed a game and never missed a practice -- in fact, she talked me out of quitting football when I was a sophomore in high school; my grandfather, who stepped into the gap when my folks were divorced; my coaches, Jerry Rhome, who rescued me off of the waiver wire in 1976; Steve Moore and Chuck Knox; Jerry Potter, my high school coach, who had the wisdom to demote me to wide receiver. They've taught me the game of football and the meaning of leadership. When I close my eyes, I can still hear their voices, hear their whistles. They still shape my character and my life.

I was one of those players, as you know, who was labeled early as "too small" and "too slow." I came to depend on people who saw me actually as bigger and faster than I really was. We all need people who believe in us. They expand the boundaries we place on our own lives. In my case, their influence did more than improve my performance in this great game; it filled a hollowness in my own life I could not explain, or even understand." – Steve Largent in his Pro Football Hall of Fame induction address

10. 10. "They're solid Americans who lead by example. Because Russell Wilson goes to Seattle Children's Hospital every Tuesday...and because they're a dominant football force that puts team first." – Actor Chris Pratt on why he loves the Seahawks

CHAPTER 4:

CATCHY NICKNAMES

QUIZ TIME!

1. What nickname does Richard Sherman go by?

    a. The Sher-Man

    b. Rick Sher

    c. Optimus Prime

    d. Bumblebee

2. Steve Largent had the nickname "Yoda."

    a. True

    b. False

3. What is Russell Wilson's nickname?

    a. Mr. Cool Under Pressure

    b. Mr. Unlimited

    c. Mr. Russ

    d. Mr. Quarterback

4. What nickname does Marshawn Lynch go by?

    a. Oakland

    b. Skittles

c. Shawny L

d. Beast Mode

5. Which is NOT a nickname the Seahawks have been referred to as a team?

    a. The Hawks

    b. The Blue Wave

    c. The Sea Birds

    d. The Legion of Boom

6. What nickname did Dave Krieg go by?

    a. Bonedirt

    b. Mudbone

    c. Bonemud

    d. Dirtbone

7. Cortez Kennedy was simply nicknamed "Tez."

    a. True

    b. False

8. What nickname did Brian Bosworth go by?

    a. Bos Man

    b. BB Gun

    c. Bosworth It

    d. The Boz

9. What was Floyd Womack's nickname?

    a. Pork Chop

    b. Beef Roast

    c. Sirloin Steak

    d. None of the Above

10. What nickname did Kam Chancellor go by?

    a. Chance
    b. Kam Kam
    c. Bam Bam
    d. Kammy

11. What nickname did Shaun Alexander go by?

    a. Mr. All-American
    b. Mr. Touchdown
    c. Mr. Tough as Nails
    d. Mr. Unlimited

12. The Seahawks cheerleaders are nicknamed "The Sea Gals."

    a. True
    b. False

13. What nickname was given to Kenny Easley?

    a. The Strongest
    b. The Defense
    c. The Interceptor
    d. The Enforcer

14. What nickname did Earl Thomas go by?

    a. Doo Doo
    b. Deuce
    c. Thom Thom
    d. Dawg

15. Doug Baldwin had the nickname "Angry Doug" during his early days as a member of the Seahawks because he always seemed to be ticked off about something.

    a. True

    b. False

16. Jeff Bryant went by the nickname _____.

    a. Hip Hop

    b. Salsa

    c. Boogie

    d. Jazz

17. The nickname given to Seahawks fans is "the 12th Man."

    a. True

    b. False

18. What is Golden Tate's nickname?

    a. Golden Child

    b. Showtime

    c. Star

    d. G – Man

19. What nickname did Ricky Watters go by?

    a. The Watter Boy

    b. Running Watter

    c. Running

    d. None of the Above

20. Jerry Rice has many nicknames including "G.O.A.T.," "World," "Flash 80" and "Gentleman Jerry."

a. True
b. False

QUIZ ANSWERS

1. C – Optimus Prime

2. A – True

3. B – Mr. Unlimited

4. D – Beast Mode

5. C – The Sea Birds

6. B – Mudbone

7. A – True

8. D – The Boz

9. A – Pork Chop

10. C – Bam Bam

11. B – Mr. Touchdown

12. A – True

13. D – The Enforcer

14. B – Deuce

15. A – True

16. C – Boogie

17. A – True

18. B – Showtime

19. C – Running

20. A – True

DID YOU KNOW?

1. "D.K." is a nickname. D.K. Metcalf's full name is DeKaylin Zecharius Metcalf.

2. Former Seahawk Jimmy Graham has the nickname "Avatar."

3. Former Seahawk Jermaine Kearse went by the nicknames "Chop Chop" and "Mr. Clutch."

4. Former Seahawk Lofa Tatupu was nicknamed "The Polynesian Lion."

5. Former Seahawk, Troymaine Pope goes by the nickname "Busta."

6. Ricardo Lockette was given the nickname "Rockette" by head coach Pete Carroll when he arrived in Seattle.

7. Former Seahawk Thomas Rawls goes by the nickname "The Train."

8. Former Seahawks kicker Stephen Hauschka goes by the nickname "Hausch Money."

9. "K.J." is a nickname. K.J. Wright's full name is Kenneth Bernard Wright Jr.

10. Former Seahawk Michael Bennett goes by the nickname "Black Santa."

CHAPTER 5:

MR. UNLIMITED

QUIZ TIME!

1. What is Russell Wilson's full name?

    a. Carrington Russell Wilson

    b. Russell Carrington Wilson

    c. James Russell Wilson

    d. Russell James Wilson

2. As of the 2020 season, Russell Wilson has played his entire NFL career with the Seahawks.

    a. True

    b. False

3. Where was Russell Wilson born?

    a. Miami, Florida

    b. San Francisco, California

    c. Cincinnati, Ohio

    d. Chicago, Illinois

4. When was Russell Wilson born?

    a. December 29, 1988
    b. December 29, 1985
    c. November 29, 1985
    d. November 29, 1988

5. Russell Wilson was drafted by MLB's Colorado Rockies in the 4th round of the 2010 MLB draft.

    a. True
    b. False

6. How many Pro Bowls has Russell Wilson been named to so far (as of the end of the 2019 season)?

    a. 1
    b. 2
    c. 5
    d. 7

7. Where did Russell Wilson go to college?

    a. North Carolina State University
    b. University of Wisconsin - Madison
    c. University of Cincinnati
    d. Both A & B

8. Russell Wilson was drafted by the Seattle Seahawks in the 3rd round of the 2012 NFL draft, 75th overall.

    a. True
    b. False

9. Which singer is Russell Wilson married to?

    a. Beyonce

    b. Rihanna

    c. Ciara

    d. Nicole Scherzinger

10. How many Super Bowls has Russell Wilson started as of the end of the 2019 season?

    a. 0

    b. 1

    c. 2

    d. 3

11. Russell Wilson is one of two quarterbacks in NFL history with a career passer rating over 100, behind _____.

    a. Steve Young

    b. Aaron Rodgers

    c. Tom Brady

    d. Joe Montana

12. Russell Wilson starred in the 2015 movie *Entourage*.

    a. True

    b. False

13. How many times has Russell Wilson been named the NFC Offensive Player of the Week (as of the end of the 2019 season)?

    a. 4

    b. 8

    c. 11

    d. 14

14. Russell Wilson and his wife, Ciara, are part of the ownership group that owns the Seattle Sounders FC Major League Soccer club.

    a. True
    b. False

15. Russell Wilson holds the NFL record for most passing yards in a playoff game by a rookie with _____.

    a. 375
    b. 385
    c. 395
    d. 405

16. In 2013, the Texas Rangers acquired Russell Wilson from the Colorado Rockies. In 2018, Wilson was traded by the Texas Rangers to the _____.

    a. Seattle Mariners
    b. Oakland A's
    c. Chicago Cubs
    d. New York Yankees

17. Russell Wilson is a 3x Steve Largent Award (given annually to Seahawks player who exemplifies the spirit, dedication, and integrity of former Seahawk, Largent) winner.

    a. True
    b. False

18. How many Super Bowls has Russell Wilson won as of the end of the 2019 season?

a. 0

b. 1

c. 2

d. 3

19. Russell Wilson currently wears the uniform No ___.

a. 1

b. 3

c. 13

d. 30

20. Russell Wilson's great-great-grandfather was a slave to a Confederate colonel and was freed after the Civil War.

a. True

b. False

QUIZ ANSWERS

1. B – Russell Carrington Wilson

2. A – True

3. C – Cincinnati, Ohio

4. D – November 29, 1988

5. A – True

6. D – 7

7. D – Both A & B

8. A – True

9. C – Ciara

10. C – 2

11. B – Aaron Rodgers

12. A – True

13. C - 11

14. A – True

15. B – 385

16. D – New York Yankees

17. A - True

18. B – 1

19. B – 3

20. A – True

DID YOU KNOW?

1. In 2016, Russell Wilson was the keynote speaker for the commencement ceremony at the University of Wisconsin – Madison.

   "I would say good luck, but I don't believe in good luck. Go make it happen. This is my story. Now it's time to write your own."

2. 2. Russell Wilson and his wife Ciara have two children together, Sienna Princess Wilson and Win Harrison Wilson. Russel is also stepfather to Ciara's son Future Zahir, whom she previously had with rapper Future.

3. 3. In September of 2018, it was announced that Russell Wilson would be the next athlete to appear on Wheaties cereal boxes.

4. 4. Russell Wilson is a senior editor for *The Players' Tribune*, which was created by New York Yankees legend Derek Jeter to give athletes a voice in the media.

5. 5. Russell Wilson is 62% African, 36% European, 1% West Asian, and 1% Central Asian.

6. 6. In high school, Russell Wilson served as his senior class president. He played football, baseball, and basketball. While a high school student, he attended the "Manning Passing Academy" football clinic run by Peyton Manning. Manning recognized Wilson years later when he was being scouted by the Denver Broncos.

7. 7. "The only issue with Russell Wilson is his height. That might be the reason he's not picked in the first couple rounds." – Jon Gruden on ESPN before the 2012 draft

8. 8. Russell Wilson was the first African-American quarterback to start in multiple Super Bowls. He is also the shortest quarterback in NFL history both to start a Super Bowl and win a Super Bowl.

9. 9. In 2012, Russell Wilson was named the Pepsi NFL Rookie of the Year.

10. 10. Russell Wilson holds the NFL record for most wins by an NFL quarterback through seven seasons (75 wins).

CHAPTER 6:

STATISTICALLY SPEAKING

QUIZ TIME!

1. Steve Largent holds the Seattle Seahawks franchise record for the most career receiving touchdowns with _____.

    a. 80
    b. 90
    c. 100
    d. 200

2. Doug Baldwin holds the franchise record for the most receiving touchdowns in a season with 14.

    a. True
    b. False

3. Shaun Alexander holds the franchise record for the most career rushing touchdowns with _____.

    a. 80
    b. 90
    c. 100
    d. 110

4. Eugene Robinson holds the franchise record for the most career solo tackles with _____.

 a. 842
 b. 942
 c. 858
 d. 958

5. Which player holds the team record for most games started all-time with 197?

 a. Russell Wilson
 b. Matt Hasselbeck
 c. Cortez Kennedy
 d. Steve Largent

6. _____ is Seattle's all-time career passing leader at 31,236 yards.

 a. Matt Hasselbeck
 b. Russell Wilson
 c. Dave Krieg
 d. Jim Zorn

7. Former Seahawks quarterback Matt Hasselbeck holds the Seattle Seahawks record for most career pass attempts with 4,250.

 a. True
 b. False

8. Curt Warner holds the Seattle Seahawks record for most rushing touchdowns in a rookie season (1983) with _____ touchdowns.

a. 10

b. 12

c. 13

d. 15

9. Joey Galloway holds the Seattle Seahawks record for most receiving yards in a rookie season with 1,039 in which year?

a. 1995

b. 1996

c. 1997

d. 1999

10. _____ holds the team record for most passing yards in a rookie season with 3,118.

a. Dave Krieg

b. Jim Zorn

c. Rick Mirer

d. Russell Wilson

11. _____ holds the franchise record for most pass attempts in a rookie season with 486.

a. Dave Krieg

b. Jim Zorn

c. Rick Mirer

d. Russell Wilson

12. Matt Hasselbeck holds the Seattle record for most pass completions in a game with 39 in total in 2009.

a. True

b. False

13. Daryl Turner holds the Seahawk record for most receiving touchdowns in a rookie season with ____ total in 1984.

    a. 9

    b. 10

    c. 11

    d. 12

14. Kenny Easley and John Harris are tied for the franchise record for most interceptions in a season with ____ each.

    a. 10

    b. 9

    c. 8

    d. 7

15. Dave Brown holds the team record for most career interceptions with ____.

    a. 40

    b. 45

    c. 50

    d. 55

16. Shaun Alexander holds the Seattle Seahawks record for most touchdowns in a game. How many touchdowns did he score in that 2002 game?

    a. 3

    b. 5

    c. 7

    d. 9

17. Shaun Alexander holds the franchise record for touchdowns scored with 112.

    a. True

    b. False

18. Norm Johnson holds the team record for field goals attempted with _____.

    a. 208

    b. 218

    c. 228

    d. 238

19. Jon Ryan holds the Seattle Seahawks record for punts with _____.

    a. 740

    b. 750

    c. 760

    d. 770

20. Joe Nash holds the team record for most seasons spent with the team at 15.

    a. True

    b. False

QUIZ ANSWERS

1. C – 100

2. A – True

3. C – 100

4. B – 942

5. D – Steve Largent

6. B – Russell Wilson

7. A – True

8. C – 13

9. A – 1995

10. D – Russell Wilson

11. C – Rick Mirer

12. A – True

13. B – 10

14. A – 10

15. C – 50

16. B – 5

17. A – True

18. C – 228

19. D – 770

20. A – True

DID YOU KNOW?

1. Russell Wilson holds the Seattle Seahawks record for most consecutive games started at 147.

2. Shaun Alexander holds the Seattle Seahawks record for points scored in a single game. He scored 30 points in a 2002 game. He also holds the franchise record for points scored in a single season with 168 in 2005.

3. Lamar Smith holds the Seattle record for career two-point conversions made with 4.

4. Jon Ryan holds the team record for most consecutive games played at 159.

5. Todd Peterson holds the Seattle Seahawks record for field goals made in a season with 34 in 1999.

6. Rick Tuten holds the franchise record for punts in a season with 108 in 1992.

7. Leon Washington holds the team record for career kick return yards at 4,398. He also holds the Seahawks record for kick returns for a touchdown in a season with 3 in 2010.

8. Russell Wilson holds the Seattle Seahawks record for pass completions in a season with 353 in 2016.

9. Jacob Green holds the franchise record for career sacks with 97.5.

10. Russell Wilson is the Seahawks' all-time passing leader with 31,236 yards; Steve Largent is the Seahawks' all-time receiving leader with 13,089 yards; Shaun Alexander is the Seahawks' all-time rushing leader with 9,429 yards.

CHAPTER 7:

THE TRADE MARKET

QUIZ TIME!

1. On February 14, 2000, the Dallas Cowboys traded _____ (as a draft pick) to the Seahawks in a draft pick switch.

    a. Mack Strong
    b. Shaun Alexander
    c. Ricky Watters
    d. Reggie Brown

2. On October 5, 2010, the Buffalo Bills traded _____ to the Seattle Seahawks in exchange for Chris Hairston and Tank Carder.

    a. Golden Tate
    b. Ricardo Lockette
    c. Tarvaris Jackson
    d. Marshawn Lynch

3. After four preseason games with the Houston Oilers, Steve Largent was going to be cut by the team. Instead, he was traded to the Seahawks and the rest is history.

a. True

b. False

4. On April 19, 1997, the _____ traded Walter Jones (as a draft pick) to the Seattle Seahawks in exchange for Warrick Dunn and Frank Middleton (as draft picks).

   a. New York Jets

   b. St. Louis Rams

   c. Tampa Bay Buccaneers

   d. Miami Dolphins

5. On July 25, 2020, the Seahawks acquired Jamal Adams from the New York Jets.

   a. True

   b. False

6. What year did the Seattle Seahawks receive Richard Sherman (as a draft pick) from the Detroit Lions?

   a. 2010

   b. 2011

   c. 2012

   d. 2013

7. As a draft pick, Kam Chancellor was traded to the Seahawks by the _____ with Robert Henderson on April 5, 2010.

   a. Carolina Panthers

   b. Pittsburgh Steelers

   c. New York Giants

   d. Detroit Lions

8. On March 17, 2010, the Seattle Seahawks acquired Chris Clemons from the _____.

   a. Indianapolis Colts
   b. Philadelphia Eagles
   c. Washington Redskins
   d. Jacksonville Jaguars

9. On March 5, 2001, the Green Bay Packers traded _____ to the Seattle Seahawks for a draft pick switch.

   a. Ricky Watters
   b. Mack Strong
   c. Matt Hasselbeck
   d. Jay Graham

10. In March of 2013, the Seahawks acquired Percy Harvin from the Buffalo Bills in a draft pick switch.

   a. True
   b. False

11. On March 18, 2010, the Seattle Seahawks acquired Charlie Whitehurst and Golden Tate (as a draft pick) in a draft pick switch from the _____.

   a. San Diego Chargers
   b. Cleveland Browns
   c. Tennessee Titans
   d. Oakland Raiders

12. On August 29, 2011, the Seahawks traded Kelly Jennings to the Cincinnati Bengals in exchange for Clinton McDonald.

a. True

b. False

13. On March 10, 2015, the Seahawks acquired Jimmy Graham for Max Unger along with a draft pick switch from the
_____.

   a. Kansas City Chiefs

   b. Green Bay Packers

   c. New Orleans Saints

   d. Chicago Bears

14. On August 30, 2014, Seattle acquired Marcus Burley from the Indianapolis Colts for a 6th-round draft pick.

   a. True

   b. False

15. On September 1, 2017, the Seahawks traded _____ to the New York Jets in exchange for Sheldon Richardson in a draft pick switch.

   a. C.J. Prosise

   b. Jon Ryan

   c. Doug Baldwin

   d. Jermaine Kearse

16. On August 22, 2017, the Seahawks acquired Matt Tobin from the _____ in a draft pick switch.

   a. Baltimore Ravens

   b. Arizona Cardinals

   c. Philadelphia Eagles

   d. Houston Texans

17. To which team did the Seahawks trade Matt Flynn on April 1, 2013, in a draft pick switch?

   a. Green Bay Packers
   b. Oakland Raiders
   c. Buffalo Bills
   d. Denver Broncos

18. On September 6, 2015, Seattle traded Christine Michael to the _____ in a draft pick switch.

   a. Dallas Cowboys
   b. Green Bay Packers
   c. Indianapolis Colts
   d. Arizona Cardinals

19. On April 3, 1995, the Seahawks acquired Ricky Proehl from the _____ in a draft pick switch.

   a. St. Louis Rams
   b. Carolina Panthers
   c. Arizona Cardinals
   d. Indianapolis Colts

20. In 2018, the Seahawks traded Richard Sherman to the San Francisco 49ers.

   a. True
   b. False

QUIZ ANSWERS

1. B – Shaun Alexander

2. D – Marshawn Lynch

3. A – True

4. C – Tampa Bay Buccaneers

5. A – True

6. B – 2011

7. D – Detroit Lions

8. B – Philadelphia Eagles

9. C – Matt Hasselbeck

10. B – False, Minnesota Vikings

11. A – San Diego Chargers

12. A – True

13. C – New Orleans Saints

14. A – True

15. D – Jermaine Kearse

16. C – Philadelphia Eagles

17. B – Oakland Raiders

18. A – Dallas Cowboys

19. C – Carolina Panthers

20. B – False (Seahawks cut Sherman and the Niners signed him three days later to a 3-year contract worth $39 million.)

DID YOU KNOW?

1. On October 19, 2004, the Seattle Seahawks traded a draft pick to the Oakland Raiders in exchange for Hall-of-Famer Jerry Rice.

2. On March 7, 2005, the Seahawks traded Trent Dilfer to the Cleveland Browns in exchange for a 4th-round draft pick.

3. On September 11, 2006, the Seahawks traded a 1st-round draft pick to the New England Patriots in exchange for Deion Branch. On October 12, 2010, the Seahawks traded Deion Branch back to the Patriots in exchange for a 4th-round draft pick.

4. On April 29, 2007, the Seattle Seahawks traded Darrell Jackson to the San Francisco 49ers in exchange for a 4th-round draft pick.

5. On September 1, 2010, Seattle traded Josh Wilson to the Baltimore Ravens in exchange for a 5th-round draft pick.

6. On August 27, 2012, the Seattle Seahawks traded Tarvaris Jackson to the Buffalo Bills in exchange for a 7th-round draft pick.

7. On March 14, 2018, the Seahawks traded Michael Bennett to the Philadelphia Eagles in exchange for Marcus Johnson and draft pick switches.

8. On October 31, 2017, the Seahawks acquired Duane Brown from the Houston Texans in a draft pick switch.

9. On September 1, 2018, the Seattle Seahawks traded Darrell Daniels to the Indianapolis Colts in exchange for Marcus Johnson.

10. On September 1, 2019, Seattle traded Jacob Martin, Barkevious Mingo and a 3rd-round draft pick to the Houston Texans in exchange for Jadeveon Clowney.

CHAPTER 8:

DRAFT DAY

QUIZ TIME!

1. With the 75th overall pick in the _____ round of the 2012 NFL draft, the Seattle Seahawks selected Russell Wilson.

    a. 2nd

    b. 3rd

    c. 4th

    d. 5th

2. With the 145th overall pick in the 5th round of the _____ NFL draft, the Seattle Seahawks selected Richard Sherman.

    a. 2009

    b. 2010

    c. 2011

    d. 2012

3. With the 12th overall pick in the 1st round of the 2007 NFL draft, the _____ selected Marshawn Lynch.

    a. Seattle Seahawks

    b. Oakland Raiders

c. San Francisco 49ers

d. Buffalo Bills

4. With the 117th overall pick in 4th round of the 1976 NFL draft, the _____ selected Steve Largent.

   a. Seattle Seahawks

   b. Houston Oilers

   c. Minnesota Vikings

   d. Tampa Bay Buccaneers

5. With the 3rd overall pick in 1st round of the _____ NFL draft, the Seahawks selected Curt Warner.

   a. 1980

   b. 1981

   c. 1983

   d. 1984

6. With the _____ overall pick in the 1st round of the 1990 NFL draft, the Seattle Seahawks selected Cortez Kennedy.

   a. 1st

   b. 2nd

   c. 3rd

   d. 4th

7. With the 6th overall pick in the 1st round of the 1997 NFL draft, Seattle selected Walter Jones.

   a. True

   b. False

8. With the _____ overall pick in the 1st round of the 1981 NFL draft, the Seattle Seahawks selected Kenny Easley.

a. 1st
b. 2nd
c. 3rd
d. 4th

9. With the 60th overall pick in the 2nd round of the _____ NFL draft, the Seattle Seahawks selected Golden Tate.

    a. 2009
    b. 2010
    c. 2012
    d. 2014

10. The Seahawks drafted Matt Hasselbeck in the 6th round, 187th overall, in the 1998 NFL draft.

    a. True
    b. False

11. With the 36th overall pick in the 2nd round of the 1994 NFL draft, the Seahawks selected _____.

    a. Kevin Mawae
    b. Trey Junkin
    c. Brian Blades
    d. Mack Strong

12. Michael Sinclair was drafted in the 6th round, 155th overall, of the 1991 NFL draft by the Seattle Seahawks.

    a. True
    b. False

13. With the 133rd overall pick in the 5th round of the 2010 NFL draft, Seattle selected _____.

a. Jon Ryan

b. Charlie Whitehurst

c. Kam Chancellor

d. Deion Branch

14. In the ____ round of the 2010 NFL draft, the Seattle Seahawks selected Earl Thomas.

    a. 8th

    b. 4th

    c. 2nd

    d. 1st

15. With the ____ overall pick in the 2nd round of the 2012 NFL draft, the Seahawks selected Bobby Wagner.

    a. 41st

    b. 45th

    c. 47th

    d. 50th

16. With the 10th overall pick in the 1st round of the 1980 NFL draft, the Seahawks selected _____.

    a. Jim Zorn

    b. Jacob Green

    c. Efren Herrera

    d. Will Lewis

17. With the 6th overall pick in the 1st round of the 1982 NFL draft, the Seattle Seahawks selected _____.

    a. Jeff Bryant

    b. Dan Doornink

c. Pete Metzelaars

d. Mike Tice

18. Dave Brown was drafted in the 1st round, 26th overall, in the 1975 NFL draft by the _____.

a. Green Bay Packers

b. Dallas Cowboys

c. San Diego Chargers

d. Pittsburgh Steelers

19. With the 27th overall pick in the 1st round of the 2018 NFL draft, the Seahawks selected Rashaad Penny out of _____.

a. UC Berkeley

b. San Diego State University

c. San Jose State University

d. Fresno State University

20. Tarvaris Jackson was selected by the Minnesota Vikings in the 2nd round, 64th overall, in the 2006 NFL draft.

a. True

b. False

QUIZ ANSWERS

1. B – 3rd

2. C – 2011

3. D – Buffalo Bills

4. B – Houston Oilers

5. C – 1983

6. C – 3rd

7. A – True

8. D – 4th

9. B – 2010

10. B – False, Green Bay Packers

11. A – Kevin Mawae

12. A – True

13. C – Kam Chancellor

14. D – 1st

15. C – 47th

16. B – Jacob Green

17. A – Jeff Bryant

18. D – Pittsburgh Steelers

19. B – San Diego State University

20. A – True

DID YOU KNOW?

1. Current Seahawk Carlos Hyde was selected by the San Francisco 49ers in the 2nd round, 57th overall, in the 2014 NFL draft.

2. Current Seahawks punter Michael Dickson was selected by the Seahawks in the 5th round, 149th overall, in the 2018 NFL draft.

3. Current Seahawk D.K. Metcalf was selected by the Seahawks in the 2nd round, 64th overall, in the 2019 NFL draft. His father, Terrence Metcalf, played for the Chicago Bears from 2002 to 2008.

4. Current Seahawk Shaquill Griffin was selected by the Seahawks in the 3rd round, 90th overall, in the 2017 NFL draft.

5. Current Seahawk K.J. Wright was selected by the team in the 4th round, 99th overall, in the 2011 NFL draft.

6. Current Seahawk Luke Willson was selected by the team in the 5th round, 158th overall, in the 2013 NFL draft.

7. Current Seahawk David Moore was selected by the Seahawks in the 7th round, 226th overall, in the 2017 NFL draft.

8. Current Seahawk Chris Carson was selected by the Seahawks in the 7th round, 249th overall, in the 2017 NFL draft.

9. Former Seahawk Jerry Rice was selected by the San Francisco 49ers in the 1st round, 16th overall, in the 1985 NFL draft.

10. Former Seahawk Shaun Alexander was selected by the Seahawks in the 1st round, 19th overall, in the 2000 NFL draft.

CHAPTER 9:

ODDS & ENDS

QUIZ TIME!

1. Which Seahawk appeared on the cover of Madden NFL 15?

    a. Russell Wilson
    b. Marshawn Lynch
    c. Richard Sherman
    d. None of the Above

2. Jerry Rice finished in the top two of the 2005-2006 season of *Dancing with the Stars*.

    a. True
    b. False

3. Eugene Robinson served as a color analyst for the _____ Radio Network from 2002-2018.

    a. Seattle Seahawks
    b. Carolina Panthers
    c. Atlanta Falcons
    d. Green Bay Packers

4. In May 2019, Marshawn Lynch was cast in the third season of _____, which premiered in 2020.

    a. Schitt's Creek
    b. The Mandalorian
    c. Stranger Things
    d. Westworld

5. After retiring from football, Dave Krieg became a _____.

    a. Real estate investor
    b. Motivational speaker
    c. Pastor
    d. Both A & B

6. Both Matt Hasselbeck and his wife have been _____.

    a. Bitten by a rattlesnake
    b. Struck by lightning
    c. To the top of Mount Everest
    d. In Broadway plays

7. Russell Wilson's twin brother, James, also played in the NFL from 2012-2015.

    a. True
    b. False

8. Which former Seahawks player was their defensive backs coach from 1992 to 1998?

    a. Kenny Easley
    b. Jacob Green

c. Dave Brown

d. None of the Above

9. Which rapper mentioned Russell Wilson in his 2013 song "The Monster"? It's payback, Russell Wilson falling way back/In the draft, turn nothing into something, still can make that/Straw into gold chump, I will spin Rumpelstiltskin in a haystack

a. Jay-Z

b. Macklemore

c. Drake

d. Eminem

10. In 2017, _____ raised the 12 Flag atop the Space Needle before the Seahawks' wild card playoff game against the Detroit Lions.

a. Dave Krieg

b. Steve Largent

c. Walter Jones

d. Joe Nash

11. _____ was the quarterbacks coach for the Seattle Seahawks from 2001-2007.

a. Warren Moon

b. Rick Mirer

c. Jim Zorn

d. Dave Krieg

12. Doug Baldwin helped establish and currently serves as a board member for the Players Coalition, an NFL player-

led organization advocating for criminal justice and education reform.

a. True

b. False

13. Curt Warner owned Curt Warner _____ in Vancouver, Washington from 1999-2010.

a. Ford

b. Chevrolet

c. Toyota

d. Nissan

14. In 2019, Lofa Tatupu founded a _____ company called ZoneIN.

a. Home Fitness

b. Protein Powder

c. CBD

d. Clothing

15. In 2015, Jon Ryan tried out for which TV competition show?

a. Survivor

b. American Ninja Warrior

c. Big Brother

d. Masterchef

16. The character "Michael" in the film *The Blind Side* starring Sandra Bullock is based on former Seahawk Michael Bennett.

a. True

b. False

17. Seahawks head coach Pete Carroll founded _____, "to restore peace, save lives and link individuals in the inner city to resources they need in order to thrive" in Los Angeles, California.

    a. A Safe LA
    b. Life, Love, LA
    c. Living LA
    d. A Better LA

18. How many children do Shaun Alexander and his wife Valerie have?

    a. 2
    b. 6
    c. 9
    d. 11

19. In 2017, Marshawn Lynch launched his own cellphone service, called _____, which allows subscribers to pay their phone bill by engaging in ads and offers.

    a. Beast Mode Mobile
    b. Beast Mobile
    c. Money Mobile
    d. Marshawn Mobile

20. D.K. Metcalf is the son of former NFL guard Terrence Metcalf.

    a. True
    b. False

QUIZ ANSWERS

1. C – Richard Sherman

2. A – True

3. B – Carolina Panthers

4. D – Westworld

5. D – Both A & B

6. B – Struck by lightning

7. B – False

8. C – Dave Brown

9. D – Eminem

10. A – Dave Krieg

11. C – Jim Zorn

12. A – True

13. B – Chevrolet

14. C – CBD

15. B – American Ninja Warrior

16. B – False, Michael Oher

17. D – A Better LA

18. C – 9

19. B – Beast Mobile

20. A – True

DID YOU KNOW?

1. Following Cortez Kennedy's death in 2017 at just 48 years old, the main drag in Wilson, Arkansas, was named for him.

2. Matt Hasselbeck's sister-in-law is TV personality and former host of *The View*, Elizabeth Hasselbeck. Elizabeth is married to Matt's brother Tim, who is also a former NFL quarterback.

3. Marshawn Lynch attended Oakland Technical High School, the same high school as Oakland Athletics MLB legend Rickey Henderson.

4. In March 2020, Russell Wilson and his wife Ciara partnered with Food Lifeline to donate 1 million meals to those in need during the COVID-19 pandemic.

5. In 2013, Richard Sherman started The Richard Sherman Family Foundation, which helps kids in low-income families receive school supplies and clothing to ensure academic success.

6. In 2002, Kenny Easley was finally elected to the Seattle Seahawks Ring of Honor after multiple attempts by the Seahawks to nominate him, but he was not interested.

7. Jon Ryan is married to comedian Sarah Colonna, who hosts a podcast and was a regular on the show *Chelsea Lately*.

8. Ricky Watters is currently a motivational speaker for kids who, like himself, are adopted. He is also a recording artist, music producer, president and CEO of Tigero Entertainment, and an author. He was the head football coach for Oak Ridge High School in Orlando, Florida, until resigning in 2013. He returned to Notre Dame in 2014 to complete the three final credits necessary for a graphic design degree.

9. Jamal Adams is a pescatarian, meaning seafood is the only type of meat that he eats in an otherwise vegetarian diet.

10. Brian Blades was charged with murder in the second degree for the death of his cousin, Charles Blades Jr., but was acquitted.

CHAPTER 10:

OFFENSE

QUIZ TIME!

1. How many Pro Bowls was Ricky Watters named to during his 10-season NFL career?

    a. 0
    b. 2
    c. 3
    d. 5

2. Doug Baldwin played his entire eight-season NFL career with the Seattle Seahawks.

    a. True
    b. False

3. During his nine-season NFL career, Shaun Alexander played for the Seattle Seahawks and the _____.

    a. San Francisco 49ers
    b. Washington Redskins
    c. Green Bay Packers
    d. Miami Dolphins

4. Jimmy Graham did NOT win a Super Bowl championship during his three seasons with the Seattle Seahawks.

    a. True

    b. False

5. What year was Warren Moon inducted into the Pro Football Hall of Fame?

    a. 2002

    b. 2004

    c. 2006

    d. 2008

6. How many touchdowns did Marshawn Lynch score during his 2014 season with the Seattle Seahawks?

    a. 10

    b. 13

    c. 14

    d. 15

7. Jermaine Kearse played his entire seven-season NFL career with the Seattle Seahawks.

    a. True

    b. False

8. Which of the following teams did former Seahawk, Dave Krieg NOT play for during his 19-season NFL career?

    a. Arizona Cardinals

    b. Detroit Lions

    c. Chicago Bears

    d. Dallas Cowboys

9. How many seasons did Jim Zorn play for the Seattle Seahawks?

    a. 5
    b. 7
    c. 9
    d. 11

10. Which of the following teams did former Seahawk, Joey Galloway NOT play for during his 16-season NFL career?

    a. Carolina Panthers
    b. New England Patriots
    c. Tampa Bay Buccaneers
    d. Dallas Cowboys

11. How many Super Bowls did Steve Largent win during his 14-season NFL career?

    a. 0
    b. 1
    c. 3
    d. 4

12. Brian Blades' brother, Bennie Blades, also played for the Seahawks.

    a. True
    b. False

13. How many Pro Bowls was Jerry Rice named to during his 21-season NFL career?

    a. 8
    b. 10

c. 13

d. 15

14. How many seasons did Golden Tate play for the Seattle Seahawks?

    a. 2

    b. 4

    c. 5

    d. 6

15. During his 14-year NFL career, Bobby Engram played for the Seattle Seahawks, Chicago Bears, and the _____.

    a. Tennessee Titans

    b. Oakland Raiders

    c. San Francisco 49ers

    d. Kansas City Chiefs

16. How many Pro Bowls was Matt Hasselbeck named to during his 17-season NFL career?

    a. 1

    b. 3

    c. 6

    d. 9

17. During his eight-season NFL career, Curt Warner played for the Seattle Seahawks and the _____.

    a. Minnesota Vikings

    b. New York Giants

    c. Los Angeles Rams

    d. Oakland Raiders

18. Which of the following teams did former Seahawk, Rick Mirer NOT play for in his eight-season NFL career?

    a. San Francisco 49ers
    b. Oakland Raiders
    c. New York Jets
    d. Minnesota Vikings

19. How many Super Bowls did Deion Branch win during his 12-season NFL career?

    a. 0
    b. 1
    c. 2
    d. 3

20. As of the end of the 2019 season, Russell Wilson has been named to six Pro Bowls.

    a. True
    b. False

QUIZ ANSWERS

1. D – 5

2. A – True

3. B – Washington Redskins

4. A – True

5. C – 2006

6. B – 13

7. B – False, Seahawks and New York Jets

8. D – Dallas Cowboys

9. C – 9

10. A – Carolina Panthers

11. A – 0

12. A – True

13. C – 13

14. B – 4

15. D – Kansas City Chiefs

16. B – 3

17. C – Los Angeles Rams

18. D – Minnesota Vikings

19. C – 2

20. A – True

DID YOU KNOW?

1. As of the end of the 2019 season, Russell Wilson has started every game for the Seahawks since his debut in 2012. So far, he has been named to six Pro Bowls and has won a Super Bowl championship.

2. Steve Largent spent his entire NFL career with the Seattle Seahawks, playing 200 games for the team. He is a member of the Pro Football Hall of Fame, a 7x Pro Bowler, 1x All-Pro, and 1988 Walter Payton Man of the Year Award. He is also a member of the HOF All-1980s team. His uniform number is retired by the Seahawks.

3. At the time of this writing, Marshawn Lynch is retired, but we all know that could change at any minute. As of the end of the 2019 season, Lynch had spent seven seasons with the Seahawks, playing 83 games for the team. He has also played for the Buffalo Bills and Oakland Raiders. He is a 1x Super Bowl champion, 5x Pro Bowler, 1x All-Pro, and member of the HOF All-2010s team.

4. Doug Baldwin played his entire NFL career with the Seattle Seahawks, playing 123 games for the team. He is a 1x Super Bowl champion and 2x Pro Bowler.

5. Golden Tate currently plays for the New York Giants. He has also played for the Detroit Lions. He spent four seasons with the Seahawks, playing 58 games for the team. So far in his career, he is a 1x Super Bowl champion and 1x Pro Bowler.

6. Shaun Alexander played eight seasons for the Seattle Seahawks and one season with the Washington Redskins. He played 119 games with the Seahawks. He is a 3x Pro Bowler, 1x All-Pro, 1x MVP, member of the HOF All-2000s team, 2005 AP Offensive Player of the Year Award winner, and 2005 Bert Bell Award winner.

7. Ricky Watters spent four seasons with Seattle, playing 53 games for the Seahawks. He also played for the San Francisco 49ers and Philadelphia Eagles. He is a 1x Super Bowl champion and 5x Pro Bowler.

8. Matt Hasselbeck spent 10 seasons with the Seahawks, playing 138 games for the team. He also played for the Green Bay Packers, Tennessee Titans, and Indianapolis Colts. He is a 3x Pro Bowler.

9. Jerry Rice spent one season with the Seattle Seahawks, playing 11 games for the team. He also played for the San Francisco 49ers and Oakland Raiders. He is a member of the Pro Football Hall of Fame, a 13x Pro Bowler, 10x All-Pro, 3x Super Bowl champion, member of the HOF All-1980's team, member of the HOF All-1990's team, 1987 AP Offensive Player of the Year Award winner, 1993 AP Offensive Player of the Year Award winner and 1987 Bert Bell Award winner.

10. Dave Krieg spent 12 seasons with the Seahawks, playing 129 games for the team. He also played for the Kansas City Chiefs, Tennessee Titans, Arizona Cardinals, Chicago Bears, and Detroit Lions. He is a 3x Pro Bowler.

CHAPTER 11:

DEFENSE

QUIZ TIME!

1. As of the 2020 season, Richard Sherman has played for two teams during NFL career. He has played for the Seattle Seahawks and the _____.

    a. Green Bay Packers
    b. Arizona Cardinals
    c. San Francisco 49ers
    d. New England Patriots

2. Kam Chancellor played his entire eight-season NFL career with the Seahawks.

    a. True
    b. False

3. How many Pro Bowls was Earl Thomas named to during his 10-season NFL career?

    a. 3
    b. 4
    c. 5
    d. 7

4. What year was Kenny Easley inducted into the Pro Football Hall of Fame?

    a. 2015
    b. 2017
    c. 2018
    d. 2019

5. How many Super Bowl championships did Eugene Robinson win in his 16-season NFL career?

    a. 0
    b. 1
    c. 3
    d. 4

6. How many seasons did Michael Bennett play for the Seattle Seahawks?

    a. 3
    b. 5
    c. 7
    d. 8

7. Marcus Trufant played his entire 10-season NFL career with Seattle Seahawks.

    a. True
    b. False

8. What year was Cortez Kennedy inducted into the Pro Football Hall of Fame?

    a. 2007
    b. 2010

c. 2012

d. 2014

9. What year was John Randle inducted into the Pro Football Hall of Fame?

   a. 2007

   b. 2010

   c. 2012

   d. 2014

10. During his seven seasons with the Seattle Seahawks, how many times was Richard Sherman named to the Pro Bowl?

    a. 1

    b. 2

    c. 4

    d. 5

11. How many Super Bowl championships did Dave Brown win during his 15-season NFL career?

    a. 0

    b. 1

    c. 2

    d. 3

12. Eugene Robinson played his entire 16-season NFL career with the Seahawks.

    a. True

    b. False

13. During his 10-season NFL career, Cliff Avril played for the Seattle Seahawks and the _____.

a. Baltimore Ravens

b. New Orleans Saints

c. Denver Broncos

d. Detroit Lions

14. During his 11-season NFL career, John Harris played for the Seattle Seahawks and the _____.

a. Minnesota Vikings

b. Atlanta Falcons

c. Houston Oilers

d. St. Louis Cardinals

15. In his 13-season NFL career, Shawn Springs played for the Seattle Seahawks, Washington Redskins, and _____.

a. Jacksonville Jaguars

b. Indianapolis Colts

c. New England Patriots

d. Pittsburgh Steelers

16. Carl Eller, who spent his final season with the Seahawks, was inducted into the Pro Football Hall of Fame in 2004.

a. True

b. False

17. How many Pro Bowls was Kam Chancellor named to during his eight-season NFL career?

a. 0

b. 2

c. 4

d. 6

18. How many Pro Bowls was John Randle named in his 14-season NFL career?

  a. 1
  b. 3
  c. 5
  d. 7

19. How many times was Kenny Easley named an All-Pro during his seven-season NFL career?

  a. 1
  b. 2
  c. 3
  d. 4

20. Aaron Curry is the brother of NBA star Stephen Curry.

  a. True
  b. False

QUIZ ANSWERS

1. C – San Francisco 49ers

2. A – True

3. D – 7

4. B – 2017

5. B – 1

6. B – 5

7. A – True

8. C – 2012

9. B – 2010

10. C – 4

11. B – 1

12. B – False (Seahawks, Atlanta Falcons, Green Bay Packers, and Carolina Panthers)

13. D – Detroit Lions

14. A – Minnesota Vikings

15. C – New England Patriots

16. A – True

17. C – 4

18. D – 7

19. C – 3

20. B – False

DID YOU KNOW?

1. Richard Sherman currently plays for the San Francisco 49ers. He spent the first seven years of his NFL career with the Seattle Seahawks, playing a total of 105 games for the team. He is a 1x Super Bowl champion, 5x Pro Bowler, 3x All-Pro, and a member of the HOF All-2010s team.

2. Cortez Kennedy spent his entire 11-season NFL career with the Seattle Seahawks, playing a total of 167 games for the team. He is a member of the Pro Football Hall of Fame, 8x Pro Bowler, a 3x All-Pro, 1992 AP Defensive Player of the Year Award winner, and a member of the HOF All-1990s Team.

3. Kam Chancellor spent his entire eight-season NFL career with the Seattle Seahawks, playing a total of 109 games for the team. He is a 4x Pro Bowler and 1x Super Bowl champion.

4. Kenny Easley spent his entire seven-season NFL career with the Seattle Seahawks, playing a total of 89 games for the team. He is a member of the Pro Football Hall of Fame, 5x Pro Bowler, 3x All-Pro, 1984 AP Defensive Player of the Year Award winner, and member of the HOF All-1980s Team.

5. Earl Thomas spent nine seasons with the Seattle Seahawks, playing a total of 125 games for the team. He also played one season with the Baltimore Ravens. He is a 7x Pro

Bowler, 3x All-Pro, 1x Super Bowl champion, and member of the HOF All-2010s Team.

6. Michael Bennett spent five seasons with the Seattle Seahawks, playing a total of 75 games for the team. He also played for the Tampa Bay Buccaneers, Dallas Cowboys, New England Patriots, and Philadelphia Eagles. He is a 3x Pro Bowler and 1x Super Bowl champion.

7. John Randle spent three seasons with the Seahawks, playing a total of 43 games for the team. He had previously played for the Minnesota Vikings for 11 seasons. He is a member of the Pro Football Hall of Fame, 7x Pro Bowler, 6x All-Pro, and a member of the HOF All-1990s Team.

8. Lofa Tatupu spent his entire five-season NFL career with the Seattle Seahawks, playing a total of 84 games for the team. He is a 3x Pro Bowler and 1x All-Pro. His father, Mosi Tatupu played in the NFL for 14 seasons.

9. Shawn Springs spent seven seasons with the Seattle Seahawks, playing a total of 93 games for the team. He also played for the Washington Redskins and New England Patriots. He is a 1x Pro Bowler.

10. Cliff Avril spent five seasons with the Seattle Seahawks, playing a total of 67 games for the team. He also spent vie seasons with the Detroit Lions. He is a 1x Pro Bowler and 1x Super Bowl champion.

CHAPTER 12:

SPECIAL TEAMS

QUIZ TIME!

1. During his 12-season NFL career, Jon Ryan played for the Seattle Seahawks and the _____.

    a. Cincinnati Bengals
    b. Green Bay Packers
    c. Denver Broncos
    d. Kansas City Chiefs

2. Jon Ryan won a Super Bowl championship with the Seattle Seahawks in 2013.

    a. True
    b. False

3. How many Pro Bowls was Norm Johnson named to during his 18-season NFL career?

    a. 0
    b. 2
    c. 4
    d. 8

4. Which of the following teams did Rick Tuten NOT play for in his 11-season NFL career?

   a. St. Louis Rams
   b. Buffalo Bills
   c. Philadelphia Eagles
   d. Denver Broncos

5. During his 10-season NFL career, Jeff West played for the Seattle Seahawks, St. Louis Cardinals and _____.

   a. Miami Dolphins
   b. Oakland Raiders
   c. San Diego Chargers
   d. New Orleans Saints

6. How many Pro Bowls was Jeff Feagles named to during his 22-season NFL career?

   a. 0
   b. 2
   c. 5
   d. 15

7. Current Seahawk Michael Dickson has been named to one Pro Bowl so far in his career (as of the end of the 2019 season).

   a. True
   b. False

8. As of the 2020 season, which of the following teams has former Seahawk Stephen Hauschka NOT played for in his career?

a. Denver Broncos

b. Buffalo Bills

c. Baltimore Ravens

d. San Francisco 49ers

9. Sebastian Janikowski played for the Seattle Seahawks for one season after playing for the _____ for 17 seasons.

   a. San Francisco 49ers

   b. Oakland Raiders

   c. New England Patriots

   d. Pittsburgh Steelers

10. How many Pro Bowls was Josh Brown named to during his 14-season NFL career?

    a. 0

    b. 1

    c. 3

    d. 5

11. Which of the following teams did former Seahawk Olindo Mare NOT play for in his 16-season NFL career?

    a. Miami Dolphins

    b. Pittsburgh Steelers

    c. New Orleans Saints

    d. Carolina Panthers

12. John Kasay was drafted by the Seahawks.

    a. True

    b. False

13. How many Super Bowls did Efren Herrera win during his eight-season NFL career?

    a. 0
    b. 1
    c. 2
    d. 3

14. Which of the following teams did former Seahawk, Todd Peterson NOT play for during his 12-season NFL career?

    a. San Francisco 49ers
    b. Arizona Cardinals
    c. Atlanta Falcons
    d. Cincinnati Bengals

15. Blair Walsh played one season with the Seattle Seahawks and five seasons with the _____.

    a. New York Jets
    b. Minnesota Vikings
    c. Detroit Lions
    d. Tampa Bay Buccaneers

16. Jon Ryan was never named to a Pro Bowl.

    a. True
    b. False

17. During his 18-season NFL career, Norm Johnson played for the Seattle Seahawks, Atlanta Falcons, Pittsburgh Steelers, and _____.

    a. Philadelphia Eagles
    b. Denver Broncos

c. Miami Dolphins

d. Oakland Raiders

18. How many Pro Bowls was Sebastian Janikowski named to during his 18-season NFL career?

    a. 0

    b. 1

    c. 3

    d. 5

19. What year was Jeff Feagles inducted into the Pro Football Hall of Fame?

    a. 2012

    b. 2016

    c. 2019

    d. He is NOT a member of the Pro Football Hall of Fame.

20. Stephen Hauschka won a Super Bowl championship with the Seattle Seahawks in 2013.

    a. True

    b. False

QUIZ ANSWERS

1. B – Green Bay Packers

2. A – True

3. B – 2

4. D – Denver Broncos

5. C – San Diego Chargers

6. B – 2

7. A – True

8. D – San Francisco 49ers

9. B – Oakland Raiders

10. B – 1

11. B – Pittsburgh Steelers

12. A – True

13. B – 1

14. D – Cincinnati Bengals

15. B – Minnesota Vikings

16. A – True

17. A – Philadelphia Eagles

18. B – 1

19. D – He is NOT a member of the Pro Football Hall of Fame.

20. A – True

DID YOU KNOW?

1. Jon Ryan spent 10 seasons with the Seattle Seahawks, playing in a total of 159 games for the team. He also played two seasons with the Green Bay Packers. He is a 1x Super Bowl champion.

2. Norm Johnson spent nine seasons with the Seattle Seahawks, playing in a total of 134 games for the team. He also played for the Atlanta Falcons, Pittsburgh Steelers, and Philadelphia Eagles. He is a 2x Pro Bowler and 1x All-Pro.

3. Jeff Feagles spent five seasons with the Seattle Seahawks, playing in a total of 80 games for the team. He also played for the New York Giants, Arizona Cardinals, Philadelphia Eagles, and New England Patriots. He is a 1x Super Bowl champion and 2x Pro Bowler.

4. Stephen Hauschka currently plays for the Jacksonville Jaguars. He spent six seasons with the Seahawks, playing in 96 games for the team. He has also played for the Buffalo Bills, Baltimore Ravens, and Denver Broncos. He is a 1x Super Bowl champion.

5. Josh Brown spent five seasons with Seattle, playing in a total of 80 games for the Seahawks. He also played for the New York Giants, St. Louis Rams, and Cincinnati Bengals. He is a 1x Pro Bowler.

6. Olindo Mare spent three seasons with the Seahawks and

played in 48 games for the team. He also spent 10 years with the Miami Dolphins and played for the Carolina Panthers, Chicago Bears, and New Orleans Saints. He is a 1x Pro Bowler and 1x All-Pro.

7. Blair Walsh spent one season with the Seattle Seahawks, playing in a total of 16 games for the team in 2017. He also played for the Minnesota Vikings. He is a 1x Pro Bowler and 1x All-Pro.

8. Michael Dickson is currently a punter for the Seattle Seahawks. He was drafted by the Seahawks in 2018. In his rookie season, he was named a Pro Bowler and All-Pro.

9. Jason Myers is currently Seattle's kicker. He previously played for the Jacksonville Jaguars and New York Jets and he is a 1x Pro Bowler.

10. Rick Tuten spent seven seasons with the Seattle Seahawks, playing in 101 games for the team. He also played for the St. Louis Rams, Buffalo Bills, and Philadelphia Eagles. He is a 1x Super Bowl champion and 1x Pro Bowler.

CHAPTER 13:

SUPER BOWL

QUIZ TIME!

1. How many Super Bowls have the Seattle Seahawks won?

    a. 0

    b. b.1

    c. c. 2

    d. d. 3

2. How many NFC Conference championships have the Seattle Seahawks won (as of the end of the 2019 season)?

    a. 3

    b. 4

    c. 6

    d. 8

3. Which team did the Seattle Seahawks face in Super Bowl XLVIII?

    a. Pittsburgh Steelers

    b. Baltimore Ravens

    c. New England Patriots

    d. Denver Broncos

4. Which team did the Seattle Seahawks face in Super Bowl XL?

    a. Indianapolis Colts
    b. Tennessee Titans
    c. Pittsburgh Steelers
    d. Kansas City Chiefs

5. Which team did the Seattle Seahawks face in Super Bowl XLIX?

    a. Pittsburgh Steelers
    b. Baltimore Ravens
    c. New England Patriots
    d. Denver Broncos

6. How many appearances have the Seattle Seahawks made in the NFL playoffs (as of the end of the 2019 season)?

    a. 15
    b. 18
    c. 20
    d. 21

7. Super Bowl XL was played at Ford Field in Detroit, Michigan.

    a. True
    b. False

8. Where was Super Bowl XLVIII played?

    a. Qualcomm Stadium, San Diego, California
    b. Lucas Oil Stadium, Indianapolis, Indiana
    c. Mercedes-Benz Stadium, Atlanta, Georgia
    d. MetLife Stadium, East Rutherford, New Jersey

9. Where was Super Bowl XLIX played?

    a. Levi's Stadium, Santa Clara, California
    b. AT&T Stadium, Arlington, Texas
    c. University of Phoenix Stadium, Glendale, Arizona
    d. Hard Rock Stadium, Miami Gardens, Florida

10. Who was Seattle's head coach during Super Bowl XL?

    a. Jim L. Mora
    b. Pete Carroll
    c. Dennis Erickson
    d. Mike Holmgren

11. Who was Seattle's head coach during Super Bowls XLVIII and XLIX?

    a. Jim L. Mora
    b. Pete Carroll
    c. Chuck Knox
    d. Mike Holmgren

12. The Seahawks won Super Bowl XLVIII by a score of 43-8.

    a. True
    b. False

13. Who played the halftime show at Super Bowl XL?

    a. Paul McCartney
    b. Prince
    c. The Rolling Stones
    d. Beyonce

14. Who played the halftime show at Super Bowl XLVIII?

    a. Jennifer Lopez and Shakira
    b. Justin Timberlake
    c. Lady Gaga
    d. Bruno Mars and the Red Hot Chili Peppers

15. Who played the halftime show at Super Bowl XLIX?

    a. Katy Perry
    b. Justin Timberlake
    c. Maroon 5
    d. Coldplay

16. Aretha Franklin, Aaron Neville, and Dr. John sang the National Anthem before Super Bowl XL.

    a. True
    b. False

17. Who sang the National Anthem before Super Bowl XLVIII?

    a. Lady Gaga
    b. Renee Fleming
    c. Alicia Keys
    d. Kelly Clarkson

18. Who sang the National Anthem before Super Bowl XLIX?

    a. Demi Lovato
    b. Pink
    c. Idina Menzel
    d. Carrie Underwood

19. The Seahawks hold the record for the quickest score in Super Bowl history when they took a 2-0 lead with 14:48 left in the first quarter. Then they scored to take a 29-0 lead with 14:48 left in the third quarter. This occurred in Super Bowl _____.

    a. XL
    b. XLVIII
    c. XLIX
    d. Both B & C

20. Former Seahawk linebacker Malcolm Smith was named Super Bowl MVP in Super Bowl XLVIII.

    a. True
    b. False

QUIZ ANSWERS

1. B – 1 (2013)

2. A – 3 (20015, 2013, 2014)

3. D – Denver Broncos

4. C – Pittsburgh Steelers

5. C – New England Patriots

6. B – 18

7. A – True

8. D - MetLife Stadium, East Rutherford, New Jersey

9. C – University of Phoenix Stadium, Glendale, Arizona

10. D – Mike Holmgren

11. B – Pete Carroll

12. A – True

13. C – The Rolling Stones

14. D – Bruno Mars and the Red Hot Chili Peppers

15. A – Katy Perry (Remember "Left Shark"???)

16. A – True

17. B – Renee Fleming

18. C – Idina Menzel

19. B – XLVIII

20. A – True

DID YOU KNOW?

1. Super Bowl XL featuring the Seahawks and Steelers was the first Super Bowl to be aired in HD (high definition) in all aspects. It was also the last Super Bowl to be aired on ABC.

2. In Super Bowl XL, the Seahawks became the first team to have their full team name painted in the end zone for a Super Bowl. "Seattle" was painted above the word "Seahawks." Usually, end zones feature only the nickname and not the geographic location.

3. NBC's broadcast of Super Bowl XLIX remains the most-watched program in the network's history, as well as the most-watched program in American TV history.

4. In Super Bowl XLVIII, the Seattle Seahawks tied for the third-largest blowout in Super Bowl history with their 43-8 victory over the Broncos.

5. Super Bowl XLVIII was the first to be broadcast in Spanish on Fox Deportes and was their highest-rated telecast outside of soccer.

6. Super Bowl XL took place on February 5, 2006. Super Bowl XLVIII took place on February 2, 2014. Super Bowl XLIX took place on February 1, 2015.

7. When the Seahawks lost Super Bowl XLIX, they became the four defending Super Bowl champion team to lose the following year's championship game.

8. The top seeds from both conferences met in both Super Bowl XLVIII and Super Bowl XLIX.

9. Super Bowl XLVIII was the first time the winning team scored over 40 points while holding its opponent to under 10 points. This was the first Super Bowl victory for the Seahawks and the fifth Super Bowl loss for the Broncos.

10. In Super Bowl XL, Tom Brady took part in the ceremonial coin toss. In Super Bowl XLVIII, Joe Namath and Phil Simms took part in the ceremonial coin toss. In Super Bowl XLIX, Kenny Easley and Tedy Bruschi took part in the ceremonial coin toss.

CHAPTER 14:

HEATED RIVALRIES

QUIZ TIME!

1. Which team does NOT play in the NFC West with the Seahawks?

    a. Arizona Cardinals

    b. San Francisco 49ers

    c. Denver Broncos

    d. Los Angeles Rams

2. The Seattle Seahawks were in the AFC West Division from 1977 to 2001.

    a. True

    b. False

3. The Seahawks have won one Super Bowl championship. How many have the San Francisco 49ers won?

    a. 1

    b. 3

    c. 5

    d. 7

4. The Seahawks have won one Super Bowl championship. How many have the Green Bay Packers won?

   a. 1
   b. 2
   c. 3
   d. 4

5. The Seahawks have won one Super Bowl championship. How many have the Denver Broncos won?

   a. 4
   b. 3
   c. 1
   d. 0

6. What is the largest 49ers victory vs the Seahawks?

   a. 38-7
   b. 41-0
   c. 48-0
   d. 38-0

7. The Seattle Seahawks have won the most NFC West Division titles.

   a. True
   b. False

8. What is the largest-ever Seahawk victory over the 49ers?

   a. 41-0
   b. 48-14
   c. 41-3
   d. 38-14

9. What is the longest 49ers win streak against the Seahawks?

  a. 3
  b. 4
  c. 8
  d. 13

10. What is the longest Seahawk win streak against the 49ers?

  a. 4
  b. 6
  c. 8
  d. 10

11. The very first game between the Seahawks and 49ers was played in _____.

  a. 1976
  b. 1980
  c. 1989
  d. 1995

12. The Seattle Seahawks and San Francisco 49ers have never met in the NFL playoffs.

  a. True
  b. False

13. Which player has NOT played for both the Seahawks and the 49ers?

  a. Richard Sherman
  b. Jerry Rice
  c. Golden Tate
  d. Ricardo Lockette

14. Which player has NOT played for both the Seahawks and the Green Bay Packers?

    a. Matt Hasselbeck
    b. Jon Ryan
    c. Dave Brown
    d. Shaun Alexander

15. In 2011, the Seahawks and 49ers rivalry intensified when Pete Carroll (former USC head coach) and _____ (former Stanford head coach) took over as the Seahawks' and 49ers' head coaches. USC and Stanford are rivals as well.

    a. Mike Singletary
    b. Jim Tomsula
    c. Kyle Shanahan
    d. Jim Harbaugh

16. The Seahawks won the one playoff meeting between the Seahawks and 49ers by a score of 23-17.

    a. True
    b. False

17. After the 2013 NFC championship game, Richard Sherman called out 49ers receiver, _____ claiming to be the "best corner in the game."

    a. Anquan Boldin
    b. Michael Crabtree
    c. Terrell Owens
    d. Jerry Rice

18. The early 2010s brought much success to both the 49ers and Seahawks due to new head coaches and freshly drafted quarterbacks. In 2012, the Seahawks drafted QB Russell Wilson. In 2011 the 49ers drafted QB _____.

    a. Alex Smith
    b. Jimmy Garoppolo
    c. Colin Kaepernick
    d. Steve Young

19. Each team in the NFC West has won at least three division titles, which makes it one of only two divisions in the NFL to do so.

    a. True
    b. False

20. Every team in the NFC West has made at least one appearance in the Super Bowl.

    a. True
    b. False

QUIZ ANSWERS

1. C – Denver Broncos

2. A – True

3. C – 5

4. D – 4

5. B – 3

6. A – 38-7 (1988)

7. B – False (San Francisco 49ers have 20.)

8. C – 41-3 (2005)

9. B – 4 (2010-2012)

10. D – 10 (2014-2018)

11. A – 1976

12. B – False (2013 NFC Championship game)

13. C – Golden Tate

14. D – Shaun Alexander

15. D – Jim Harbaugh

16. A – True

17. B – Michael Crabtree

18. C – Colin Kaepernick

19. A – True

20. A – True

DID YOU KNOW?

1. The San Francisco 49ers have won the most NFC West championships with 20 as of the end of the 2019 season. The Los Angeles Rams have 15, the Seahawks have 8, and the Arizona Cardinals have 3.

2. From 2010 to 2014, either the Seahawks or 49ers won the NFC West championship.

3. As of the time of this writing, the Seahawks lead their all-time series with the 49ers by 25-17.

4. In the final week of the 2019 season, the 49ers beat the Seahawks to claim the division title and NFC top seed. They made it all the way to the Super Bowl.

5. From 1970 to 2000, the 49ers led the season series against the Seahawks by 4-2. In the 2000s, the Seahawks led the season series against the 49ers by 10-6. In the 2010s, the Seahawks led the season series against the 49ers by 14-7.

6. The NFC was realigned in 2002. The Falcons, Panthers, and Saints moved to the NFC South, the Cardinals moved in from the NFC East, and the Seahawks returned from the AFC West.

7. The 2016 season marked the first time neither the Seahawks nor the 49ers played a division game east of the Rocky Mountains.

8. Since realignment in 2002, the Seahawks have led the NFC West in wins, division titles, and playoff appearances.

9. The Seahawks won four straight division titles from 2004 through 2007, while the 49ers finished in third or fourth place each season and did not have a winning season from 2003 through 2010.

10. "(49ers coach Kyle Shanahan's) culture and the way he did things was very similar to how we did things in Seattle, and what I was accustomed to," he says. "That made a huge difference. Hey, I can get this $20 million guaranteed and be in Detroit and lose football games. Or I can go to a place where I'm very comfortable with the scheme, coach, and culture, and I'm very comfortable with the things they do, and I really believe we can win." - Richard Sherman on his choice to sign with the 49ers after being cut by the Seahawks.

CHAPTER 15:

THE AWARDS SECTION

QUIZ TIME!

1. Which Seahawk won the 2012 Pepsi NFL Rookie of the Year Award?

    a. Golden Tate
    b. Russell Wilson
    c. Doug Baldwin
    d. Kam Chancellor

2. The Seattle Seahawks' wide receivers won the 2019 Bud Light Celly of the Year Award for their *NSYNC "Bye Bye Bye" endzone dance.

    a. True
    b. False

3. Which Seattle Seahawks player won a Walter Payton NFL Man of the Year Award in 1988?

    a. Dave Krieg
    b. Curt Warner
    c. Norm Johnson
    d. Steve Largent

4. Which Seahawks player won the Steve Largent Award in 2000?

   a. Cortez Kennedy
   b. Mack Strong
   c. Ricky Watters
   d. Shaun Alexander

5. Which Seahawks player won the Bert Bell Award in 2005?

   a. Shaun Alexander
   b. Matt Hasselbeck
   c. Bobby Engram
   d. Walter Jones

6. Which current Seahawks player hosted the 2020 ESPN ESPY Awards show?

   a. D.K. Metcalf
   b. Tyler Lockett
   c. Bobby Wagner
   d. Russell Wilson

7. Jack Patera won the 1978 AP NFL Coach of the Year Award.

   a. True
   b. False

8. Which former Seahawks head coach won *Sporting News'* NFL Coach of the Year in 1984?

   a. Jack Patera
   b. Mike McCormack
   c. Chuck Knox
   d. Tom Flores

9. Which former Seahawk won the 2005 *Sporting News* NFL Player of the Year Award?

   a. Matt Hasselbeck
   b. Shaun Alexander
   c. Mack Strong
   d. Lofa Tatupu

10. Which Seahawk won the very first Bart Starr Award in 1989?

    a. Dave Krieg
    b. Brian Blades
    c. Steve Largent
    d. Eugene Robinson

11. Which former Seahawk won the 2003 Bart Starr Award?

    a. Mack Strong
    b. Trent Dilfer
    c. Matt Hasselbeck
    d. Shawn Springs

12. Cortez Kennedy won the 1996 Steve Largent Award.

    a. True
    b. False

13. How many Steve Largent Awards did Mack Strong win in his career?

    a. 3
    b. 4
    c. 5
    d. 6

14. Which Seahawk was named the 2013 Super Bowl MVP?

    a. Byron Maxwell
    b. Malcolm Smith
    c. Kam Chancellor
    d. Marshawn Lynch

15. Who is the only Seahawks player to ever win the ESPN ESPY for Best NFL Player?

    a. Russell Wilson
    b. Marshawn Lynch
    c. Richard Sherman
    d. Shaun Alexander

16. Russell Wilson won the 2018 Kids Choice Sports Award for "Best Cannon," beating out Dak Prescott, Aaron Rodgers, Clayton Kershaw, Justin Verlander, and Corey Kluber.

    a. True
    b. False

17. Which former Seahawk won the 1992 AP Defensive Player of the Year Award?

    a. Eugene Robinson
    b. Cortez Kennedy
    c. Jeff Bryant
    d. Joe Nash

18. Which Seahawk won the 2019 Secret Game Changer Award?

    a. Jadeveon Clowney
    b. Rashaad Penny

c. Shaquem Griffin

d. D.K. Metcalf

19. Which of the following celebrities has NOT hosted the NFL Honors Awards Show (as of the 2019 season)?

    a. Alec Baldwin

    b. Jimmy Fallon

    c. Seth Meyers

    d. Steve Harvey

20. Russell Wilson hosted the Nickelodeon Kids Choice Sports Awards show in 2015, 2016, and 2017.

    a. True

    b. False

QUIZ ANSWERS

1. B – Russell Wilson

2. A – True

3. D – Steve Largent

4. C – Ricky Watters

5. A – Shaun Alexander

6. D – Russell Wilson

7. A – True

8. C – Chuck Knox

9. B – Shaun Alexander

10. C – Steve Largent

11. B – Trent Dilfer

12. True

13. C – 5

14. B – Malcolm Smith

15. D – Shaun Alexander (2006)

16. A – True

17. B – Cortez Kennedy

18. C – Shaquem Griffin

19. B – Jimmy Fallon

20. A – True

DID YOU KNOW?

1. Steve Largent Award winners so far include Largent himself, Jacob Green, Rufus Porter, Jeff Bryant, Joe Nash, Eugene Robinson, Brian Blades, Terry Wooden, Cortez Kennedy, Winston Moss, Michael Sinclair, Chad Brown, Ricky Watters, Mack Strong (x5), Trent Dilfer, Bobby Engram, Mike Holmgren, Matt Hasselbeck, Roy Lewis, Red Bryant, Russell Wilson (x3), Earl Thomas, Kam Chancellor (x2), Bobby Wagner, and Richard Sherman.

2. In 2014, Seahawks head coach Pete Carroll was nominated for the ESPY for Best Coach. That same year, he was presented with the Jack Horrigan Award. Although he has yet to be named NFL Coach of the Year, he did win a Pac-10 Coach of the Year Award in 2006.

3. Russell Wilson is 11x NFC Offensive Player of the Week Award winner, 2014 Good Guy Award winner, NFC Offensive Player of the Month (September 2020), NFL Offensive Rookie of the Month (December 2012), 2016 Offensive Player of the Year finalist, 7x FedEx Air Player of the Week, and NFC Rookie of the Week (Week 10 in 2012).

4. The NFL hosts an NFL Honors show each year to give out awards like MVP, Rookie of the Year, and Coach of the Year. NFL Honors debuted in Indianapolis in 2012. It is hosted in the city that is hosting the Super Bowl on the

network that is carrying that year's championship game.

5. Shaun Alexander is the only Seahawks player to ever win an AP NFL MVP Award. He won the honor in 2005.

6. Malcolm Smith was the first defensive player to win the Super Bowl MVP award since Dexter Jackson in Super Bowl XXXVII. He is one of seven defensive players to win Super Bowl MVP honors.

7. Steve Largent is the only Seahawks player ever to win the Walter Payton NFL Man of the Year Award. Largent won the honor in 1988.

8. Shaun Alexander is the only Seahawks player ever to win a Bert Bell Award. He won the honor in 2005.

9. Numbers retired by the Seattle Seahawks include The Fans (#12), Kenny Easley (#45), Walter Jones (#71), Steve Largent (#80), and Cortez Kennedy (#96).

10. The Seattle Seahawks Ring of Honor contains Dave Brown, Kenny Easley, Jacob Brown, Pete Gross, Walter Jones, Cortez Kennedy, Chuck Knox, Dave Krieg, Steve Largent, Curt Warner, Jim Zorn, and Paul Allen.

CHAPTER 16:

EMERALD CITY

QUIZ TIME!

1. What is the name of the famous observation tower at the Seattle Center?

   a. Stratosphere Tower
   b. Tower of the Americas
   c. Space Needle
   d. Reunion Tower

2. Seattle is home to the world's first Starbucks store in Pike Place Market.

   a. True
   b. False

3. People in Seattle buy more _____ per capita than any other U.S. city.

   a. Umbrellas
   b. Fish
   c. Coffee
   d. Sunglasses

4. Which musician is NOT from Seattle?

    a. Macklemore
    b. Mariah Carey
    c. Kenny G
    d. Sir Mix-a-Lot

5. Which actor from *The Office* is from Seattle?

    a. John Krasinksi (Jim)
    b. Steve Carell (Michael)
    c. Rainn Wilson (Dwight)
    d. Jenna Fischer (Pam)

6. Which of the following companies was founded in Seattle?

    a. Apple
    b. Boeing
    c. Coca Cola
    d. None of the Above

7. Seattle was the first major American city to have a female mayor.

    a. True
    b. False

8. What is the name of the famous movie starring Tom Hanks and Meg Ryan that was set in Seattle?

    a. An Officer and a Gentleman
    b. 10 Things I Hate About You
    c. You've Got Mail
    d. Sleepless in Seattle

9. What is the name of Seattle's MLB team?

   a. Seattle Sting Rays
   b. Seattle Sox
   c. Seattle Mariners
   d. Seattle Angels

10. What is the name of Seattle's former NBA team?

   a. Seattle Bulls
   b. Seattle SuperSonics
   c. Seattle Warriors
   d. Seattle Thunder

11. What is the name of the Mariners' stadium?

   a. Minute Maid Park
   b. T-Mobile Park
   c. Seattle Stadium
   d. Fenway Park

12. Seattle has a WNBA team called the Seattle Storm.

   a. True
   b. False

13. What is the name of the brand-new NHL team in Seattle?

   a. Seattle Sharks
   b. Seattle Golden Knights
   c. Seattle Metropolitans
   d. Seattle Kraken

14. What is the name of Seattle's MLS team?

   a. Seattle Dynamo
   b. Seattle Earthquakes

    c. Seattle Sounders

    d. Seattle Rapids

15. The largest man-made island in the United States is Seattle's _____.

    a. Whidbey Island

    b. Shaw Island

    c. Blake Island

    d. Harbor Island

16. Seattle's Pier 52 is the busiest ferry terminal in the United States.

    a. True

    b. False

17. What is the name of the largest public park in Seattle with 11.81 miles of walking trails?

    a. Seward Park

    b. Carkeek Park

    c. Green Lake Park

    d. Discovery Park

18. What is Seattle-Tacoma International Airport's code?

    a. STA

    b. SEA

    c. SET

    d. TAC

19. More people _____ to work in Seattle than in any other city in the United States.

a. Bike

b. Walk

c. Drive

d. Skateboard

20. Seattle is the rainiest city in the United States.

a. True

b. False

QUIZ ANSWERS

1. C – Space Needle

2. A – True

3. D – Sunglasses

4. B – Mariah Carey

5. C – Rainn Wilson (Dwight)

6. B – Boeing

7. A – True

8. D – Sleepless in Seattle

9. C – Seattle Mariners

10. B – Seattle SuperSonics

11. B – T - Mobile Park

12. A – True

13. D – Seattle Kraken

14. C – Seattle Sounders

15. D – Harbor Island

16. A – True

17. D – Discovery Park

18. B – SEA

19. A – Bike

20. B – False

DID YOU KNOW?

1. Seattle is ranked as the most literate city in the United States. It also has the highest percentage of residents with a college degree.

2. The Seattle Public Library system has the highest percentage of library card holders per capita in the United States.

3. Seattle's Pacific Northwest Ballet Company has the highest per-capita attendance in the United States. Seattle has the second-most live performances in the United States, after New York City.

4. Online retailer juggernaut Amazon was founded in Seattle in 1994.

5. Seattle was home to America's very first gas station.

6. Seattle has the largest houseboat population in the United States. In fact, the houseboat from *Sleepless in Seattle* sold for over $2 million.

7. Seattle City Light is a public utility company that powers 90% of the city via hydroelectricity, which has zero carbon footprint. The city vows to be carbon-neutral by 2050.

8. Seattle is home to Nintendo of America and Microsoft Game Studios, plus Pokémon headquarters is nearby. Seattle is incredibly important to the video game industry.

9. The Evergreen Point Floating Bridge is the longest floating bridge in the world at 15,580 feet long.

10. Pike Place Market is one of the oldest continuously operated farmers markets in the United States. It gets 10 million visitors annually and is the 33rd most visited tourist attraction in the world.

CHAPTER 17:

BEAST MODE

QUIZ TIME!

1. Where was Marshawn Lynch born?

    a. Detroit, Michigan
    b. Seattle, Washington
    c. Oakland, California
    d. San Diego, California

2. Marshawn Lynch played his entire career with the Seattle Seahawks.

    a. True
    b. False

3. Where did Marshawn Lynch attend college?

    a. Sacramento State University
    b. Stanford University
    c. San Diego State University
    d. UC Berkeley

4. What is Lynch's favorite candy?

    a. Starburst
    b. Skittles
    c. Sour Patch Kids
    d. Swedish Fish

5. What is Lynch's favorite restaurant?

    a. Red Robin
    b. The Cheesecake Factory
    c. Applebee's
    d. IHOP

6. How many Super Bowls has Marshawn Lynch won, as of the end of the 2019 season?

    a. 0
    b. 1
    c. 2
    d. 3

7. Marshawn Lynch was named the PAC-12 Offensive Player of the Year in 2006.

    a. True
    b. False

8. How many Pro Bowls has Marshawn Lynch been named to (as of the end of the 2019 season)?

    a. 2
    b. 3
    c. 5
    d. 7

9. How many times in his career did Lynch lead the NFL in rushing touchdowns?

    a. 0

    b. 1

    c. 2

    d. 3

10. In which TV comedy did Marshawn Lynch appear, playing a spoof of himself?

    a. Schitt's Creek

    b. Brooklyn Nine-Nine

    c. Modern Family

    d. The Good Place

11. Marshawn Lynch holds the Seattle Seahawks record for most playoff games scoring at least one touchdown with ___.

    a. 4

    b. 5

    c. 6

    d. 7

12. Lynch is a co-owner of the Oakland Panthers, of the IFL (Indoor Football League).

    a. True

    b. False

13. What year was Lynch named a First-Team All-Pro?

    a. 2012

    b. 2012

c. 2014

d. 2015

14. What uniform number did Marshawn Lynch wear as a member of the Seahawks?

    a. 20

    b. 23

    c. 24

    d. 34

15. What age was Marshawn Lynch when he made his NFL debut?

    a. 20

    b. 21

    c. 22

    d. 23

16. Marshawn Lynch was named to the Pro Football Hall of Fame All-2010's team.

    a. True

    b. False

17. In high school, Marshawn Lynch was a 4-sport athlete. He participated in football, track, basketball and _____ _____.

    a. Baseball

    b. Tennis

    c. Volleyball

    d. Wrestling

18. What did Marshawn Lynch major in at UC Berkeley?

    a. Journalism

    b. Social welfare

    c. Business

    d. Engineering

19. What was Marshawn Lynch's nickname in college?

    a. Shawny

    b. Skittles

    c. Money

    d. Beast Mode

20. Marshawn Lynch holds the UC Berkeley record for most 100-yard rushing games with 17.

    a. True

    b. False

QUIZ ANSWERS

1. C – Oakland, California

2. B – False (Seahawks, Buffalo Bills, and Oakland Raiders)

3. D – UC Berkeley

4. B – Skittles

5. C – Applebee's

6. B – 1

7. A – True

8. C – 5

9. C – 2 (2013 & 2014)

10. B – Brooklyn Nine-Nine

11. D – 7

12. A – True

13. B – 2012

14. C – 24

15. B – 21

16. A –True

17. D – Wrestling

18. B – Social Welfare

19. C – Money

20. A – True

DID YOU KNOW?

1. Marshawn Lynch has many NFL relatives including cousin Robert Jordan, cousin JaMarcus Russell, cousin Josh Johnson, and uncle Lorenzo Lynch who played in the NFL for 11 seasons.

2. Marshawn Lynch is known for being reluctant to talk to the media. In 2013, he was fined $50,000 by the NFL for refusing to talk to journalists throughout the season.

3. In 2016, Marshawn Lynch retired from the NFL. He came out of retirement in 2017 to play for the Oakland Raiders, saying that he wanted kids from Oakland to be able to see a homegrown player play for the team before their impending move to Las Vegas.

4. Lynch owns a bar-restaurant in Emeryville, California called *Rob Ben's*. Both the restaurant and Lynch were featured on an episode of *Bar Rescue* in 2020.

5. Lynch was drafted by the Buffalo Bills in the first round of the 2007 NFL draft, 12th overall.

6. Marshawn Lynch is the second all-time career rusher in UC Berkeley history.

7. Marshawn Lynch was ranked at No. 14 on the list of NFL Top 100 Players of 2014. He was ranked at No. 9 on the list of NFL Top 100 Players of 2015.

8. In 2017, Lynch became the 31st player in NFL history to rush for over 10,000 rushing yards.

9. In 2006, Marshawn Lynch was named a First Team All-American and First Team All-Pac-10.

10. "I'm just here so I won't get fined." – Marshawn Lynch

CHAPTER 18:

YODA

QUIZ TIME!

1. Where was Steve Largent born?

    a. Tampa, Florida
    b. Phoenix, Arizona
    c. Tulsa, Oklahoma
    d. Dallas, Texas

2. Steve Largent was inducted into the Pro Football Hall of Fame in his first year of eligibility, becoming the first Seahawk ever to accomplish that.

    a. True
    b. False

3. Steve Largent played for two NFL teams in his career; the Seahawks and the _____ (as a practice squad member only).

    a. New England Patriots
    b. Pittsburgh Steelers
    c. San Francisco 49ers
    d. Houston Oilers

4. Where did Steve Largent attend college?

    a. University of Notre Dame
    b. University of Tulsa
    c. Clemson University
    d. Penn State University

5. How many Pro Bowls was Steve Largent named to?

    a. 3
    b. 5
    c. 7
    d. 9

6. Steve Largent was named the NFL Man of the Year in

    _____.

    a. 1985
    b. 1986
    c. 1987
    d. 1988

7. Largent was the first player to ever catch 100 touchdown passes in the NFL.

    a. True
    b. False

8. How many times did Largent lead the NFL in receiving yards?

    a. 0
    b. 1
    c. 2
    d. 4

9. Steve Largent was named a First Team All-Pro in _____.

   a. 1984
   b. 1985
   c. 1986
   d. 1988

10. In 1999, Steve Largent ranked at No. _____ on Sporting News' list of the 100 Greatest Football Players. He was the only Seahawk to make the list.

   a. 16
   b. 26
   c. 36
   d. 46

11. What year was Steve Largent inducted into the Pro Football Hall of Fame?

   a. 1993
   b. 1995
   c. 1997
   d. 1999

12. Steve Largent is a member of the Seahawks Ring of Honor.

   a. True
   b. False

13. How many times was Steve Largent named a Second Team All-Pro?

   a. 0
   b. 2
   c. 4
   d. 5

14. Steve Largent's uniform No. ____ is retired by the Seattle Seahawks. He was the first Seahawks player to have his number retired by the team.

    a. 60
    b. 70
    c. 80
    d. 90

15. Steve Largent's uniform No. _____ is retired by the University of Tulsa.

    a. 63
    b. 73
    c. 80
    d. 83

16. Steve Largent ran for Governor of Oklahoma in 2002.

    a. True
    b. False

17. Steve Largent won the Bart Starr Award (given to the NFL player who "best exemplifies outstanding character and leadership in the home, on the field, and in the community") in _____.

    a. 1984
    b. 1985
    c. 1988
    d. 1989

18. When Steve Largent retired, he was the owner of all major career NFL receiving records.

a. True

b. False

19. How many Super Bowl championships did Steve Largent win?

    a. 0

    b. 1

    c. 2

    d. 3

20. Steve Largent served in the United States House of Representatives for Oklahoma's 1st district from 1994 through 2002.

    a. True

    b. False

QUIZ ANSWERS

1. C – Tulsa, Oklahoma

2. A – True

3. D – Houston Oilers

4. B – University of Tulsa

5. C – 7

6. D – 1988

7. A – True

8. C – 2 (1979 & 1985)

9. B – 1985

10. D – 46

11. B – 1995

12. A – True

13. C – 4 (1978, 1979, 1984 and 1987)

14. C – 80

15. D – 83

16. A – True

17. D – 1989

18. A – True

19. A – 0

20. A – True

DID YOU KNOW?

1. In 1989, Steve Largent became the first Seahawks player to win the Steve Largent Award, given annually to the Seahawks player who best exemplifies his spirit, dedication, and integrity.

2. Steve Largent was named to the NFL's 100th Anniversary All-Time Team in 2019.

3. Steve Largent was named to the 1980s All-Decade Team.

4. Although Largent's No. 80 was retired in 1992, Jerry Rice and Largent had a conversation in 2004 in which Largent allowed Rice to wear his number for the season. Jerry Rice's No. 80 is now retired by the San Francisco 49ers.

5. In 2002, Steve Largent lost his bid for Governor of Oklahoma to Brad Henry by just under 7,000 votes.

6. In November 2003, Steve Largent became the president and CEO of CTIA - The Wireless Association. CTIA is a nonprofit that represents all sectors of wireless communications. He held this position until May 2014.

7. In 1996, Steve Largent was named to the list of *People Magazine*'s "Most Beautiful People."

8. During his NFL career, Largent was given the nickname "Yoda" due to his ability to catch anything that was thrown at him.

9. From 1991 to 1994, Largent worked as a marketing consultant for the Sara Lee Corporation.

10. Steve Largent Award winners so far include Largent himself, Jacob Green, Rufus Porter, Jeff Bryant, Joe Nash, Eugene Robinson, Brian Blades, Terry Wooden, Cortez Kennedy, Winston Moss, Michael Sinclair, Chad Brown, Ricky Watters, Mack Strong (x5), Trent Dilfer, Bobby Engram, Mike Holmgren, Matt Hasselbeck, Roy Lewis, Red Bryant, Russell Wilson (x3), Earl Thomas, Kam Chancellor (x2), Bobby Wagner, and Richard Sherman.

CONCLUSION

Learn anything new? Now you truly are the ultimate Seahawks fan! Not only did you learn about the Hawks of the modern era but you also expanded your knowledge back to the early days of the franchise.

You learned about the Seahawks' origins and history. You learned about the history of their uniforms and jersey numbers, you identified some famous quotes, and read some of the craziest nicknames of all time. You learned more about star quarterback Russell Wilson. You also learned about the always fun Marshawn Lynch and the legendary Steve Largent.

You were amazed by Seahawks stats and recalled some of the most famous Seahawks trades, drafts, and draft picks of all time. You broke down your knowledge by offense, defense, and special teams. You looked back on the Seahawks' championship, playoff feats, and the awards that came before, after, and during them. You also learned about the Seahawks' fiercest rivalries both within their division and outside it.

Every team in the NFL has a storied history, but the Seahawks have one of the most memorable of all. They have won a treasured Lombard Trophy with the backing of their devoted fans. Being the ultimate Seahawks fan takes knowledge and a whole lot of patience, which you tested with this book. Whether you knew every answer or were stumped by several questions, you learned some of the most interesting history that the game of football has to offer.

The deep history of the Seahawks represents what we all love about the game of football: the heart, the determination, the tough times, and the unexpected moments, plus the players who inspire us and encourage us to do our best because, even if you get knocked down, there is always another game and another (Sun)day.

With players like Russell Wilson, D.K. Metcalf and Tyler Lockett, the future for the Seahawks continues to look bright. They have a lot to prove but there is no doubt that this franchise will continue to be one of the most competitive teams in the NFL year after year.

It's a new decade, which means there is a clean slate, ready to continue writing the history of the Seattle Seahawks. The ultimate Seahawks fan cannot wait to see what's to come for their beloved Hawks.

14477832R00090